Hive Management History Series: No. 86

The Principles of
Scientific Management

BY

FREDERICK WINSLOW TAYLOR, M.E., Sc.D.

PAST PRESIDENT OF THE AMERICAN SOCIETY OF
MECHANICAL ENGINEERS

EASTON
HIVE PUBLISHING COMPANY
1985

INTRODUCTION

PRESIDENT ROOSEVELT, in his address to the Governors at the White House, prophetically remarked that "The conservation of our national resources is only preliminary to the larger question of national efficiency."

The whole country at once recognized the importance of conserving our material resources and a large movement has been started which will be effective in accomplishing this object. As yet, however, we have but vaguely appreciated the importance of "the larger question of increasing our national efficiency."

We can see our forests vanishing, our water-powers going to waste, our soil being carried by floods into the sea; and the end of our coal and our iron is in sight. But our larger wastes of human effort, which go on every day through such of our acts as are blundering, ill-directed, or inefficient, and which Mr. Roosevelt refers to as a lack of "national efficiency," are less visible, less tangible, and are but vaguely appreciated.

We can see and feel the waste of material things. Awkward, inefficient, or ill-directed movements of men, however, leave nothing visible or tangible behind them. Their appreciation calls for an act of memory, an effort of the imagination. And for this reason, even though our daily loss from this source is greater than from our waste of material things, the one has stirred us deeply, while the other has moved us but little.

As yet there has been no public agitation for "greater national efficiency," no meetings have been called to consider how this is to be brought about. And still there are signs that the need for greater efficiency is widely felt.

The search for better, for more competent men, from the presidents of our great companies down to our household servants, was never more vigorous than it is now. And more than ever before is the demand for competent men in excess of the supply.

What we are all looking for, however, is the ready-made, competent man; the man whom some one else has trained. It is only when we fully realize that our duty, as well as our opportunity, lies in systematically cooperating to train and to make this competent man, instead of in hunting for a man whom some one else has trained, that we shall be on the road to national efficiency.

In the past the prevailing idea has been well expressed in the saying that "Captains of industry are born, not made"; and the theory has been that if one could get the right man, methods could be safely left to him. In the future it will be appreciated that our leaders must be trained right as well as born right, and that no great man can (with the old system of personal management) hope to compete with a number of ordinary men who have been properly organized so as efficiently to cooperate.

In the past the man has been first; in the future the system must be first. This in no sense, however, implies that great men are not needed. On the contrary, the first object of any good system must be that of developing first-class men; and under systematic management the best man rises to the top more certainly and more rapidly than ever before.

This paper has been written:

First. To point out, through a series of simple illustrations, the great loss which the whole country is suffering through inefficiency in almost all of our daily acts.

Second. To try to convince the reader that the remedy for this inefficiency lies in systematic management, rather than in searching for some unusual or extraordinary man.

Third. To prove that the best management is a true science, resting upon clearly defined laws, rules, and principles, as a foundation. And further to show that the fundamental principles of scientific management are applicable to all kinds of human activities, from our simplest individual acts to the work of our great corporations, which call for the most elaborate cooperation. And, briefly, through a series of illustrations, to convince the reader that whenever these principles are correctly applied, results must follow which are truly astounding.

This paper was originally prepared for presentation to The American Society of Mechanical Engineers. The illustrations chosen are such as, it is believed, will especially appeal to engineers and to managers of industrial and manufacturing establishments, and also quite as much to all of the men who are working in these establishments. It is hoped, however, that it will be clear to other readers that the same principles can be applied with equal force to all social activities: to the management of our homes; the management of our farms; the management of the business of our tradesmen, large and small; of our churches, our philanthropic institutions, our universities, and our governmental departments.

The Principles of Scientific Management

CHAPTER I

FUNDAMENTALS OF SCIENTIFIC MANAGEMENT

THE principal object of management should be to secure the maximum prosperity for the employer, coupled with the maximum prosperity for each employé.

The words "maximum prosperity" are used, in their broad sense, to mean not only large dividends for the company or owner, but the development of every branch of the business to its highest state of excellence, so that the prosperity may be permanent.

In the same way maximum prosperity for each employé means not only higher wages than are usually received by men of his class, but, of more importance still, it also means the development of each man to his state of maximum efficiency, so that he may be able to do, generally speaking, the highest grade of work for which his natural abilities fit him, and it further means giving him, when possible, this class of work to do.

It would seem to be so self-evident that maximum prosperity for the employer, coupled with maximum prosperity for the employé, ought to be the two leading objects of management, that even to state this fact should be unnecessary. And yet there is no question that, throughout the industrial world, a large part of the organization of employers, as well as employés, is for war rather than for peace, and that perhaps the majority on either side do not believe that it is possible so to arrange their mutual relations that their interests become identical.

The majority of these men believe that the fundamental interests of employés and employers are necessarily antagonistic. Scientific management, on the contrary, has for its very foundation the firm conviction that the true interests of the two are one and the same; that prosperity for the employer cannot exist through a long term of years unless it is accompanied by prosperity for the employé, and *vice versa;* and that it is possible to give the workman what he most wants — high wages — and the employer what he wants — a low labor cost — for his manufactures.

It is hoped that some at least of those who do not sympathize with each of these objects may be led to modify their views; that some employers, whose attitude toward their workmen has been that of trying to get the largest amount of work out of them for the smallest possible wages, may be led to see that a more liberal policy toward their men will pay them better; and that some of those workmen who begrudge a fair and even a large profit to their employers, and who feel that all of the fruits of their labor should belong to them, and that those for whom they work and the capital invested in the business are entitled to little or nothing, may be led to modify these views.

No one can be found who will deny that in the case of any single individual the greatest prosperity can exist only when that individual has reached his highest state of efficiency; that is, when he is turning out his largest daily output.

The truth of this fact is also perfectly clear in the case of two men working together. To illustrate: if you and your workman have become so skilful that you and he together are making two pairs of shoes in a day, while your competitor and his workman are making only one pair, it is clear that after selling your two pairs of shoes you can pay your workman much higher wages than your competitor who produces only one pair of shoes is able to pay his man, and that there will still be enough money left over for you to have a larger profit than your competitor.

In the case of a more complicated manufacturing establishment, it should also be perfectly clear that the greatest permanent prosperity for the workman, coupled with the greatest prosperity for the employer, can be brought about only when the work of the establishment is done with the smallest combined expenditure of human effort, plus nature's resources, plus the cost for the use of capital in the shape of machines, buildings, etc. Or, to state the same thing in a different way: that the greatest prosperity can exist only as the result of the greatest possible productivity of the men and machines of the establishment — that is, when each man and each machine are turning out the largest possible output; because unless your men and your machines are daily turning out more work than others around you, it is clear that competition will prevent your paying higher wages to your workmen than are paid to those of your competitor. And what is true as to the possibility of paying high wages in the case of two companies competing close beside one another is also true as to whole districts of the country and even as to nations which are in competition. In a word, that maximum prosperity can exist only as the result of maximum productivity. Later in this paper illustrations will be given of several companies which are earning large dividends and at the same time paying from 30 per cent. to 100 per cent. higher wages to their men than are paid to similar men immediately around them, and with whose employers they are in competition. These illustrations will cover different types of work, from the most elementary to the most complicated.

If the above reasoning is correct, it follows that the most important object of both the workmen and the management should be the training and development of each individual in the establishment, so that he can do (at his fastest pace and with the maximum of efficiency) the highest class of work for which his natural abilities fit him.

These principles appear to be so self-evident that many men may think it almost childish to state them.   Let us, however, turn to the facts, as they actually exist in this country and in England. The English and American peoples are the greatest sportsmen in the world.   Whenever an American workman plays baseball, or an English workman plays cricket, it is safe to say that he strains every nerve to secure victory for his side.   He does his very best to make the largest possible number of runs.   The universal sentiment is so strong that any man who fails to give out all there is in him in sport is branded as a "quitter," and treated with contempt by those who are around him.

When the same workman returns to work on the following day, instead of using every effort to turn out the largest possible amount of work, in a majority of the cases this man deliberately plans to do as little as he safely can — to turn out far less work than he is well able to do — in many instances to do not more than one-third to one-half of a proper day's work.   And in fact if he were to do his best to turn out his largest possible day's work, he would be abused by his fellow-workers for so doing, even more than if he had proved himself a "quitter" in sport.   Underworking, that is, deliberately working slowly so as to avoid doing a full day's work, "soldiering," as it is called in this country, "hanging it out," as it is called in England, "ca canae," as it is called in Scotland, is almost universal in industrial establishments, and prevails also to a large extent in the building trades; and the writer asserts without fear of contradiction that this constitutes the greatest evil with which the working-people of both England and America are now afflicted.

It will be shown later in this paper that doing away with slow working and "soldiering" in all its forms and so arranging the relations between employer and employé that each workman will work to his very best advantage and at his best speed, accompanied by the intimate cooperation with the management and the help (which the workman should receive) from the management, would result on the average in nearly doubling the output of each man and each machine. What other reforms, among those which are being discussed by these two nations, could do as much toward promoting prosperity, toward the diminution of poverty, and the alleviation of suffering? America and England have been recently agitated over such subjects as the tariff, the control of the large corporations on the one hand, and of hereditary power on the other hand, and over various more or less socialistic proposals for taxation, etc. On these subjects both peoples have been profoundly stirred, and yet hardly a voice has been raised to call attention to this vastly greater and more important subject of "soldiering," which directly and powerfully affects the wages, the prosperity, and the life of almost every working-man, and also quite as much the prosperity of every industrial establishment in the nation.

The elimination of "soldiering" and of the several causes of slow working would so lower the cost of production that both our home and foreign markets would be greatly enlarged, and we could compete on more than even terms with our rivals. It would remove one of the fundamental causes for dull times, for lack of employment, and for poverty, and therefore would have a more permanent and far-reaching effect upon these misfortunes than any of the curative remedies that are now being used to soften their consequences. It would insure higher wages and make shorter working hours and better working and home conditions possible.

Why is it, then, in the face of the self-evident fact that maximum prosperity can exist only as the result of the determined effort of each workman to turn out each day his largest possible day's work, that the great majority of our men are deliberately doing just the opposite, and that even when the men have the best of intentions their work is in most cases far from efficient?

There are three causes for this condition, which may be briefly summarized as:

First. The fallacy, which has from time immemorial been almost universal among workmen, that a material increase in the output of each man or each machine in the trade would result in the end in throwing a large number of men out of work.

Second. The defective systems of management which are in common use, and which make it necessary for each workman to soldier, or work slowly, in order that he may protect his own best in-terests.

Third. The inefficient rule-of-thumb methods, which are still almost universal in all trades, and in practising which our workmen waste a large part of their effort.

This paper will attempt to show the enormous gains which would result from the substitution by our workmen of scientific for rule-of-thumb methods.

To explain a little more fully these three causes:

First. The great majority of workmen still believe that if they were to work at their best speed they would be doing a great injustice to the whole trade by throwing a lot of men out of work, and yet the history of the development of each trade shows that each improvement, whether it be the invention of a new machine or the introduction of a better method, which results in increasing the productive capacity of the men in the trade and cheapening the costs, instead of throwing men out of work make in the end work for more men.

The cheapening of any article in common use almost immediately results in a largely increased demand for that article. Take the case of shoes, for instance. The introduction of machinery for doing every element of the work which was formerly done by hand has resulted in making shoes at a fraction of their former labor cost, and in selling them so cheap that now almost every man, woman, and child in the working-classes buys one or two pairs of shoes per year, and wears shoes all the time, whereas formerly each workman bought perhaps one pair of shoes every five years, and went barefoot most of the time, wearing shoes only as a luxury or as a matter of the sternest necessity. In spite of the enormously increased output of shoes per workman, which has come with shoe machinery, the demand for shoes has so increased that there are relatively more men working in the shoe industry now than ever before.

The workmen in almost every trade have before them an object lesson of this kind, and yet, because they are ignorant of the history of their own trade even, they still firmly believe, as their fathers did before them, that it is against their best interests for each man to turn out each day as much work as possible.

Under this fallacious idea a large proportion of the workmen of both countries each day deliberately work slowly so as to curtail the output. Almost every labor union has made, or is contemplating making, rules which have for their object curtailing the output of their members, and those men who have the greatest influence with the working-people, the labor leaders as well as many people with philanthropic feelings who are helping them, are daily spreading this fallacy and at the same time telling them that they are overworked.

A great deal has been and is being constantly said about "sweat-shop" work and conditions. The writer has great sympathy with those who are overworked, but on the whole a greater sympathy for those who are *under paid*. For every individual, however, who is overworked, there are a hundred who intentionally underwork — greatly underwork — every day of their lives, and who for this reason deliberately aid in establishing those conditions which in the end inevitably result in low wages. And yet hardly a single voice is being raised in an endeavor to correct this evil.

As engineers and managers, we are more intimately acquainted with these facts than any other class in the community, and are therefore best fitted to lead in a movement to combat this fallacious idea by educating not only the workmen but the whole of the country as to the true facts.   And yet we are practically doing nothing in this direction, and are leaving this field entirely in the hands of the labor agitators (many of whom are misinformed and misguided), and of sentimentalists who are ignorant as to actual working conditions.

Second. As to the second cause for soldiering — the relations which exist between employers and employés under almost all of the systems of management which are in common use — it is impossible in a few words to make it clear to one not familiar with this problem why it is that the *ignorance of employers* as to the proper time in which work of various kinds should be done makes it for the interest of the workman to "soldier."

The writer therefore quotes herewith from a paper read before The American Society of Mechanical Engineers, in June, 1903, entitled "Shop Management," which it is hoped will explain fully this cause for soldiering:

"This loafing or soldiering proceeds from two causes. First, from the natural instinct and tendency of men to take it easy, which may be called natural soldiering. Second, from more intricate second thought and reasoning caused by their relations with other men, which may be called systematic soldiering.

"There is no question that the tendency of the average man (in all walks of life) is toward working at a slow, easy gait, and that it is only after a good deal of thought and observation on his part or as a result of example, conscience, or external pressure that he takes a more rapid pace.

"There are, of course, men of unusual energy, vitality, and ambition who naturally choose the fastest gait, who set up their own standards, and who work hard, even though it may be against their best interests. But these few uncommon men only serve by forming a contrast to emphasize the tendency of the average.

"This common tendency to 'take it easy' is greatly increased by bringing a number of men together on similar work and at a uniform standard rate of pay by the day.

"Under this plan the better men gradually but surely slow down their gait to that of the poorest and least efficient. When a naturally energetic man works for a few days beside a lazy one, the logic of the situation is unanswerable.

'Why should I work hard when that lazy fellow gets the same pay that I do and does only half as much work?'

"A careful time study of men working under these conditions will disclose facts which are ludicrous as well as pitiable.

"To illustrate: The writer has timed a naturally energetic workman who, while going and coming from work, would walk at a speed of from three to four miles per hour, and not infrequently trot home after a day's work. On arriving at his work he would immediately slow down to a speed of about one mile an hour. When, for example, wheeling a loaded wheelbarrow, he would go at a good fast pace even up hill in order to be as short a time as possible under load, and immediately on the return walk slow down to a mile an hour, improving every opportunity for delay short of actually sitting down. In order to be sure not to do more than his lazy neighbor, he would actually tire himself in his effort to go slow.

"These men were working under a foreman of good reputation and highly thought of by his employer, who, when his attention was called to this state of things, answered: 'Well, I can keep them from sitting down, but the devil can't make them get a move on while they are at work.'

"The natural laziness of men is serious, but by far the greatest evil from which both workmen and employers are suffering is the *systematic soldiering* which is almost universal under all of the ordinary schemes of management and which results from a careful study on the part of the workmen of what will promote their best interests.

"The writer was much interested recently in hearing one small but experienced golf caddy boy of twelve explaining to a green caddy, who had shown special energy and interest, the necessity of going slow and lagging behind his man when he came up to the ball, showing him that since they were paid by the hour, the faster they went the less money they got, and finally telling him that if he went too fast the other boys would give him a licking.

"This represents a type of *systematic soldiering* which is not, however, very serious, since it is done with the knowledge of the employer, who can quite easily break it up if he wishes.

"The greater part of the *systematic soldiering*, however, is done by the men with the deliberate object of keeping their employers ignorant of how fast work can be done.

"So universal is soldiering for this purpose that hardly a competent workman can be found in a large establishment, whether he works by the day or on piece work, contract work, or under any of the ordinary systems, who does not devote a considerable part of his time to studying just how slow he can work and still convince his employer that he is going at a good pace.

"The causes for this are, briefly, that practically all employers determine upon a maximum sum which they feel it is right for each of their classes of employees to earn per day, whether their men work by the day or piece.

"Each workman soon finds out about what this figure is for his particular case, and he also realizes that when his employer is convinced that a man is capable of doing more work than he has done, he will find sooner or later some way of compelling him to do it with little or no increase of pay.

"Employers derive their knowledge of how much of a given class of work can be done in a day from either their own experience, which has frequently grown hazy with age, from casual and unsystematic observation of their men, or at best from records which are kept, showing the quickest time in which each job has been done. In many cases the employer will feel almost certain that a given job can be done faster than it has been, but he rarely cares to take the drastic measures necessary to force men to do it in the quickest time, unless he has an actual record proving conclusively how fast the work can be done.

"It evidently becomes for each man's interest, then, to see that no job is done faster than it has been in the past. The younger and less experienced men are taught this by their elders, and all possible persuasion and social pressure is brought to bear upon the greedy and selfish men to keep them from making new records which result in temporarily increasing their wages, while all those who come after them are made to work harder for the same old pay.

"Under the best day work of the ordinary type,

when accurate records are kept of the amount of work done by each man and of his efficiency, and when each man's wages are raised as he improves, and those who fail to rise to a certain standard are discharged and a fresh supply of carefully selected men are given work in their places, both the natural loafing and systematic soldiering can be largely broken up. This can only be done, however, when the men are thoroughly convinced that there is no intention of establishing piece work even in the remote future, and it is next to impossible to make men believe this when the work is of such a nature that they believe piece work to be practicable. In most cases their fear of making a record which will be used as a basis for piece work will cause them to soldier as much as they dare.

"It is, however, under piece work that the art of systematic soldiering is thoroughly developed; after a workman has had the price per piece of the work he is doing lowered two or three times as a result of his having worked harder and increased his output, he is likely entirely to lose sight of his employer's side of the case and become imbued with a grim determination to have no more cuts if soldiering can prevent it. Unfortunately for the character of the workman, soldiering involves a deliberate attempt to mislead and deceive his employer, and thus upright and straightforward workmen are compelled to become more or less hypocritical. The employer is soon looked upon as an antagonist, if not an enemy, and the mutual confidence which should exist between a leader and his men, the enthusiasm, the feeling that they are all working for the same end and will share in the results is entirely lacking.

"The feeling of antagonism under the ordinary piece-work system becomes in many cases so marked on the part of the men that any proposition made by their employers, however reasonable, is looked upon with suspicion, and soldiering becomes such a fixed habit that men will frequently take pains to restrict the product of machines which they are running when even a large increase in output would involve no more work on their part."

Third. As to the third cause for slow work, considerable space will later in this paper be devoted to illustrating the great gain, both to employers and employés, which results from the substitution of scientific for rule-of-thumb methods in even the smallest details of the work of every trade. The enormous saving of time and therefore increase in the output which it is possible to effect through eliminating unnecessary motions and substituting fast for slow and inefficient motions for the men working in any of our trades can be fully realized only after one has personally seen the improvement which results from a thorough motion and time study, made by a competent man.

To explain briefly: owing to the fact that the workmen in all of our trades have been taught the details of their work by observation of those immediately around them, there are many different ways in common use for doing the same thing, perhaps forty, fifty, or a hundred ways of doing each act in each trade, and for the same reason there is a great variety in the implements used for each class of work. Now, among the various methods and implements used in each element of each trade there is always one method and one implement which is quicker and better than any of the rest. And this one best method and best implement can only be discovered or developed through a scientific study and analysis of all of the methods and implements in use, together with accurate, minute, motion and time study. This involves the gradual substitution of science for rule of thumb throughout the mechanic arts.

This paper will show that the underlying philosophy of all of the old systems of management in common use makes it imperative that each workman shall be left with the final responsibility for doing his job practically as he thinks best, with comparatively little help and advice from the management. And it will also show that because of this isolation of workmen, it is in most cases impossible for the men working under these systems to do their work in accordance with the rules and laws of a science or art, even where one exists.

The writer asserts as a general principle (and he proposes to give illustrations tending to prove the fact later in this paper) that in almost all of the mechanic arts the science which underlies each act of each workman is so great and amounts to so much that the workman who is best suited to actually doing the work is incapable of fully understanding this science, without the guidance and help of those who are working with him or over him, either through lack of education or through insufficient mental capacity. In order that the work may be done in accordance with scientific laws, it is necessary that there shall be a far more equal division of the responsibility between the management and the workmen than exists under any of the ordinary types of management. Those in the management whose duty it is to develop this science should also guide and help the workman in working under it, and should assume a much larger share of the responsibility for results than under usual conditions is assumed by the management.

The body of this paper will make it clear that, to work according to scientific laws, the management must take over and perform much of the work which is now left to the men; almost every act of the workman should be preceded by one or more preparatory acts of the management which enable him to do his work better and quicker than he otherwise could. And each man should daily be taught by and receive the most friendly help from those who are over him, instead of being, at the one extreme, driven or coerced by his bosses, and at the other left to his own unaided devices.

This close, intimate, personal cooperation between the management and the men is of the essence of modern scientific or task management.

It will be shown by a series of practical illustrations that, through this friendly cooperation, namely, through sharing equally in every day's burden, all of the great obstacles (above described) to obtaining the maximum output for each man and each machine in the establishment are swept away. The 30 per cent. to 100 per cent. increase in wages which the workmen are able to earn beyond what they receive under the old type of management, coupled with the daily intimate shoulder to shoulder contact with the management, entirely removes all cause for soldiering. And in a few years, under this system, the workmen have before them the object lesson of seeing that a great increase in the output per man results in giving employment to more men, instead of throwing men out of work, thus completely eradicating the fallacy that a larger output for each man will throw other men out of work.

It is the writer's judgment, then, that while much can be done and should be done by writing and talking toward educating not only workmen, but all classes in the community, as to the importance of obtaining the maximum output of each man and each machine, it is only through the adoption of modern scientific management that this great problem can be finally solved. Probably most of the readers of this paper will say that all of this is mere theory. On the contrary, the theory, or philosophy, of scientific management is just beginning to be understood, whereas the management itself has been a gradual evolution, extending over a period of nearly thirty years. And during this time the employés of one company after another, including a large range and diversity of industries, have gradually changed from the ordinary to the scientific type of management. At least 50,000 workmen in the United States are now employed under this system; and they are receiving from 30 per cent. to 100 per cent. higher wages daily than are paid to men of similar caliber with whom they are surrounded, while the companies employing them are more prosperous than ever before. In these companies the output, per man and per machine, has on an average been doubled. During all these years there has never been a single strike among the men working under this system. In place of the suspicious watchfulness and the more or less open warfare which characterizes the ordinary types of management, there is universally friendly cooperation between the management and the men.

Several papers have been written, describing the expedients which have been adopted and the details which have been developed under scientific management and the steps to be taken in changing from the ordinary to the scientific type. But unfortunately most of the readers of these papers have mistaken the mechanism for the true essence. Scientific management fundamentally consists of certain broad general principles, a certain philosophy, which can be applied in many ways, and a description of what any one man or men may believe to be the best mechanism for applying these general principles should in no way be confused with the principles themselves.

It is not here claimed that any single panacea exists for all of the troubles of the working-people or of employers. As long as some people are born lazy or inefficient, and others are born greedy and brutal, as long as vice and crime are with us, just so long will a certain amount of poverty, misery, and unhappiness be with us also. No system of management, no single expedient within the control of any man or any set of men can insure continuous prosperity to either workmen or employers. Prosperity depends upon so many factors entirely beyond the control of any one set of men, any state, or even any one country, that certain periods will inevitably come when both sides must suffer, more or less. It is claimed, however, that under scientific management the intermediate periods will be far more prosperous, far happier, and more free from discord and dissension. And also, that the periods will be fewer, shorter and the suffering less. And this will be particularly true in any one town, any one section of the country, or any one state which first substitutes the principles of scientific management for the rule of thumb.

That these principles are certain to come into general use practically throughout the civilized world, sooner or later, the writer is profoundly convinced, and the sooner they come the better for all the people.

CHAPTER II

THE PRINCIPLES OF SCIENTIFIC MANAGEMENT

THE writer has found that there are three questions uppermost in the minds of men when they become interested in scientific management.

First. Wherein do the principles of scientific management differ essentially from those of ordinary management?

Second. Why are better results attained under scientific management than under the other types?

Third. Is not the most important problem that of getting the right man at the head of the company? And if you have the right man cannot the choice of the type of management be safely left to him?

One of the principal objects of the following pages will be to give a satisfactory answer to these questions.

THE FINEST TYPE OF ORDINARY MANAGEMENT

Before starting to illustrate the principles of scientific management, or "task management" as it is briefly called, it seems desirable to outline what the writer believes will be recognized as the best type of management which is in common use. This is done so that the great difference between the best of the ordinary management and scientific management may be fully appreciated.

In an industrial establishment which employs say from 500 to 1000 workmen, there will be found in many cases at least twenty to thirty different trades. The workmen in each of these trades have had their knowledge handed down to them by word of mouth, through the many years in which their trade has been developed from the primitive condition, in which our far-distant ancestors each one practised the rudiments of many different trades, to the present state of great and growing subdivision of labor, in which each man specializes upon some comparatively small class of work.

The ingenuity of each generation has developed quicker and better methods for doing every element of the work in every trade. Thus the methods which are now in use may in a broad sense be said to be an evolution representing the survival of the fittest and best of the ideas which have been developed since the starting of each trade. However, while this is true in a broad sense, only those who are intimately acquainted with each of these trades are fully aware of the fact that in hardly any element of any trade is there uniformity in the methods which are used. Instead of having only one way which is generally accepted as a standard, there are in daily use, say, fifty or a hundred different ways of doing each element of the work. And a little thought will make it clear that this must inevitably be the case, since our methods have been handed down from man to man by word of mouth, or have, in most cases, been almost unconsciously learned through personal observation. Practically in no instances have they been codified or systematically analyzed or described. The ingenuity and experience of each generation — of each decade, even, have without doubt handed over better methods to the next. This mass of rule-of-thumb or traditional knowledge may be said to be the principal asset or possession of every tradesman. Now, in the best of the ordinary types of management, the managers recognize frankly the fact that the 500 or 1000 workmen, included in the twenty to thirty trades, who are under them, possess this mass of traditional knowledge, a large part of which is not in the possession of the management. The management, of course, includes foremen and superintendents, who themselves have been in most cases first-class workers at their trades. And yet these foremen and superintendents know, better than any one else, that their own knowledge and personal skill falls far short of the combined knowledge and dexterity of all the workmen under them. The most experienced managers therefore frankly place before their workmen the problem of doing the work in the best and most economical way. They recognize the task before them as that of inducing each workman to use his best endeavors, his hardest work, all his traditional knowledge, his skill, his ingenuity, and his good-will — in a word, his "initiative," so as to yield the largest possible return to his employer. The problem before the management, then, may be briefly said to be that of obtaining the best *initiative* of every workman. And the writer uses the word "initiative" in its broadest sense, to cover all of the good qualities sought for from the men.

On the other hand, no intelligent manager would hope to obtain in any full measure the initiative of his workmen unless he felt that he was giving them something more than they usually receive from their employers. Only those among the readers of this paper· who have been managers or who have worked themselves at a trade realize how far the average workman falls short of giving his employer his full initiative. It is well within the mark to state that in nineteen out of twenty industrial establishments the workmen believe it to be directly against their interests to give their employers their best initiative, and that instead of working hard to do the largest possible amount of work and the best quality of work for their employers, they deliberately work as slowly as they dare while they at the same time try to make those over them believe that they are working fast.[1]

The writer repeats, therefore, that in order to have any hope of obtaining the initiative of his workmen the manager must give some *special incentive* to his men beyond that which is given to the average of the trade. This incentive can be given in several different ways, as, for example,

[1] The writer has tried to make the reason for this unfortunate state of things clear in a paper entitled "Shop Management," read before the American Society of Mechanical Engineers."

the hope of rapid promotion or advancement; higher wages, either in the form of generous piece-work prices or of a premium or bonus of some kind for good and rapid work; shorter hours of labor; better surroundings and working conditions than are ordinarily given, etc., and, above all, this special incentive should be accompanied by that personal consideration for, and friendly contact with, his workmen which comes only from a genuine and kindly interest in the welfare of those under him. It is only by giving a special inducement or "incentive" of this kind that the employer can hope even approximately to get the "initiative" of his workmen. Under the ordinary type of management the necessity for offering the workman a special inducement has come to be so generally recognized that a large proportion of those most interested in the subject look upon the adoption of some one of the modern schemes for paying men (such as piece work, the premium plan, or the bonus plan, for instance) as practically the whole system of management. Under scientific management, however, the particular pay system which is adopted is merely one of the subordinate elements.

Broadly speaking, then, the best type of management in ordinary use may be defined as management in which the workmen give their best *initiative* and in return receive some *special incentive* from their employers. This type of management will be referred to as the management of "*initiative and incentive*" in contradistinction to scientific management, or task management, with which it is to be compared.

The writer hopes that the management of "initiative and incentive" will be recognized as representing the best type in ordinary use, and in fact he believes that it will be hard to persuade the average manager that anything better exists in the whole field than this type. The task which the writer has before him, then, is the difficult one of trying to prove in a thoroughly convincing way that there is another type of management which is not only better but overwhelmingly better than the management of "initiative and incentive."

The universal prejudice in favor of the management of "initiative and incentive" is so strong that no mere theoretical advantages which can be pointed out will be likely to convince the average manager that any other system is better. It will be upon a series of practical illustrations of the actual working of the two systems that the writer will depend in his efforts to prove that scientific management is so greatly superior to other types. Certain elementary principles, a certain philosophy, will however be recognized as the essence of that which is being illustrated in all of the practical examples which will be given. And the broad principles in which the scientific system differs from the ordinary or "rule-of-thumb" system are so simple in their nature that it seems desirable to describe them before starting with the illustrations.

Under the old type of management success depends

almost entirely upon getting the "initiative" of the workmen, and it is indeed a rare case in which this initiative is really attained. Under scientific management the "initiative" of the workmen (that is, their hard work, their good-will, and their ingenuity) is obtained with absolute uniformity and to a greater extent than is possible under the old system; and in addition to this improvement on the part of the men, the managers assume new burdens, new duties, and responsibilities never dreamed of in the past. The managers assume, for instance, the burden of gathering together all of the traditional knowledge which in the past has been possessed by the workmen and then of classifying, tabulating, and reducing this knowledge to rules, laws, and formulæ which are immensely helpful to the workmen in doing their daily work. In addition to developing a *science* in this way, the management take on three other types of duties which involve new and heavy burdens for themselves.

These new duties are grouped under four heads:

First. They develop a science for each element of a man's work, which replaces the old rule-of-thumb method.

Second. They scientifically select and then train, teach, and develop the workman, whereas in the past he chose his own work and trained himself as best he could.

Third. They heartily coopcrate with the men so as to insure all of the work being done in accordance with the principles of the science which has been developed.

Fourth. There is an almost equal division of the work and the responsibility between the management and the workmen. The management take over all work for which they are better fitted than the workmen, while in the past almost all of the work and the greater part of the responsibility were thrown upon the men.

It is this combination of the initiative of the workmen, coupled with the new types of work done by the management, that makes scientific management so much more efficient than the old plan.

Three of these elements exist in many cases, under the management of "initiative and incentive," in a small and rudimentary way, but they are, under this management, of minor importance, whereas under scientific management they form the very essence of the whole system.

The fourth of these elements, "an almost equal division of the responsibility between the management and the workmen," requires further explanation. The philosophy of the management of "initiative and incentive" makes it necessary for each workman to bear almost the entire responsibility for the general plan as well as for each detail of his work, and in many cases for his implements as well. In addition to this he must do all of the actual physical labor. The development of a science, on the other hand, involves the establishment of many rules, laws, and formulæ which replace the judgment of the individual workman and which can be effectively used only after having been systematically recorded, indexed, etc. The practical use of scientific data also calls for a room in which to keep the books, records,[1] etc., and a desk for the planner to work at. Thus all of the planning which under the old system was done by the workman, as a result of his personal experience, must of necessity under the new system be done by the management in accordance with the laws of the science; because even if the workman was well suited to the development and use of scientific data, it would be physically impossible for him to work at his machine and at a desk at the same time. It is also clear that in most cases one type of man is needed to plan ahead and an entirely different type to execute the work.

The man in the planning room, whose specialty under scientific management is planning ahead, invariably finds that the work can be done better and more economically by a subdivision of the labor; each act of each mechanic, for example, should be preceded by various preparatory acts done by other men. And all of this involves, as we have said, "an almost equal division of the responsibility and the work between the management and the workman."

To summarize: Under the management of "initiative and incentive" practically the whole problem is "up to the workman," while under scientific management fully one-half of the problem is "up to the management."

---

[1] For example, the records containing the data used under scientific management in an ordinary machine-shop fill thousands of pages.

Perhaps the most prominent single element in modern scientific management is the task idea. The work of every workman is fully planned out by the management at least one day in advance, and each man receives in most cases complete written instructions, describing in detail the task which he is to accomplish, as well as the means to be used in doing the work. And the work planned in advance in this way constitutes a task which is to be solved, as explained above, not by the workman alone, but in almost all cases by the joint effort of the workman and the management. This task specifies not only what is to be done but how it is to be done and the exact time allowed for doing it. And whenever the workman succeeds in doing his task right, and within the time limit specified, he receives an addition of from 30 per cent. to 100 per cent. to his ordinary wages. These tasks are carefully planned, so that both good and careful work are called for in their performance, but it should be distinctly understood that in no case is the workman called upon to work at a pace which would be injurious to his health. The task is always so regulated that the man who is well suited to his job will thrive while working at this rate during a long term of years and grow happier and more prosperous, instead of being overworked. Scientific management consists very largely in preparing for and carrying out these tasks.

The writer is fully aware that to perhaps most of the readers of this paper the four elements which differentiate the new management from the old will at first appear to be merely high-sounding phrases; and he would again repeat that he has no idea of convincing the reader of their value merely through announcing their existence. His hope of carrying conviction rests upon demonstrating the tremendous force and effect of these four elements through a series of practical illustrations. It will be shown, first, that they can be applied absolutely to all classes of work, from the most elementary to the most intricate; and second, that when they are applied, the results must of necessity be overwhelmingly greater than those which it is possible to attain under the management of initiative and incentive.

The first illustration is that of handling pig iron, and this work is chosen because it is typical of perhaps the crudest and most elementary form of labor which is performed by man. This work is done by men with no other implements than their hands. The pig-iron handler stoops down, picks up a pig weighing about 92 pounds, walks for a few feet or yards and then drops it on to the ground or upon a pile. This work is so crude and elementary in its nature that the writer firmly believes that it would be possible to train an intelligent gorilla so as to become a more efficient pig-iron handler than any man can be. Yet it will be shown that the science of handling pig iron is so great and amounts to so much that it is impossible for the man who is best suited to this type of work to understand the principles of this science, or even to work in accordance with these principles without the aid of a man better educated than he is.   And the further illustrations to be given will make it clear that in almost all of the mechanic arts the science which underlies each workman's act is so great and amounts to so much that the workman who is best suited actually to do the work is incapable (either through lack of education or through insufficient mental capacity) of understanding this science.   This is announced as a general principle, the truth of which will become apparent as one illustration after another is given. After showing these four elements in the handling of pig iron, several illustrations will be given of their application to different kinds of work in the field of the mechanic arts, at intervals in a rising scale, beginning with the simplest and ending with the more intricate forms of labor.

One of the first pieces of work undertaken by us, when the writer started to introduce scientific management into the Bethlehem Steel Company, was to handle pig iron on task work.   The opening of the Spanish War found some 80,000 tons of pig iron placed in small piles in an open field adjoining the works.   Prices for pig iron had been so low that it could not be sold at a profit, and it therefore had been stored.   With the opening of the Spanish War the price of pig iron rose, and this large accumulation of iron was sold.   This gave us a good opportunity to show the workmen, as well as the owners and managers of the works, on a fairly large scale the advantages of task work over the old-fashioned day work and piece work, in doing a very elementary class of work.

The Bethlehem Steel Company had five blast furnaces, the product of which had been handled by a pig-iron gang for many years. This gang, at this time, consisted of about 75 men. They were good, average pig-iron handlers, were under an excellent foreman who himself had been a pig-iron handler, and the work was done, on the whole, about as fast and as cheaply as it was anywhere else at that time.

A railroad switch was run out into the field, right along the edge of the piles of pig iron. An inclined plank was placed against the side of a car, and each man picked up from his pile a pig of iron weighing about 92 pounds, walked up the inclined plank and dropped it on the end of the car.

We found that this gang were loading on the average about $12\frac{1}{2}$ long tons per man per day. We were surprised to find; after studying the matter, that a first-class pig-iron handler ought to handle between 47[1] and 48 long tons per day, instead of $12\frac{1}{2}$ tons. This task seemed to us so very large that we were obliged to go over our work several times before we were absolutely sure that we were right. Once we were sure, however, that 47 tons was a proper day's work for a first-class pig-iron handler, the task which faced us as managers under the modern scientific plan was clearly before us. It was our duty to see that the 80,000 tons of pig

[1] See foot-note at foot of page 60.

iron was loaded on to the cars at the rate of 47 tons per man per day, in place of $12\frac{1}{2}$ tons, at which rate the work was then being done. And it was further our duty to see that this work was done without bringing on a strike among the men, without any quarrel with the men, and to see that the men were happier and better contented when loading at the new rate of 47 tons than they were when loading at the old rate of $12\frac{1}{2}$ tons.

Our first step was the scientific selection of the workman. In dealing with workmen under this type of management, it is an inflexible rule to talk to and deal with only one man at a time, since each workman has his own special abilities and limitations, and since we are not dealing with men in masses, but are trying to develop each individual man to his highest state of efficiency and prosperity. Our first step was to find the proper workman to begin with. We therefore carefully watched and studied these 75 men for three or four days, at the end of which time we had picked out four men who appeared to be physically able to handle pig iron at the rate of 47 tons per day. A careful study was then made of each of these men. We looked up their history as far back as practicable and thorough inquiries were made as to the character, habits, and the ambition of each of them. Finally we selected one from among the four as the most likely man to start with. He was a little Pennsylvania Dutchman who had been observed to trot back home for a mile or so after his work in the evening.

about as fresh as he was when he came trotting down to work in the morning. We found that upon wages of $1.15 a day he had succeeded in buying a small plot of ground, and that he was engaged in putting up the walls of a little house for himself in the morning before starting to work and at night after leaving. He also had the reputation of being exceedingly "close," that is, of placing a very high value on a dollar. As one man whom we talked to about him said, "A penny looks about the size of a cart-wheel to him." This man we will call Schmidt.

The task before us, then, narrowed itself down to getting Schmidt to handle 47 tons of pig iron per day and making him glad to do it. This was done as follows. Schmidt was called out from among the gang of pig-iron handlers and talked to somewhat in this way:

"Schmidt, are you a high-priced man?"

"Vell, I don't know vat you mean."

"Oh yes, you do. What I want to know is whether you are a high-priced man or not."

"Vell, I don't know vat you mean."

"Oh, come now, you answer my questions. What I want to find out is whether you are a high-priced man or one of these cheap fellows here. What I want to find out is whether you want to earn $1.85 a day or whether you are satisfied with $1.15, just the same as all those cheap fellows are getting."

"Did I vant $1.85 a day? Vas dot a high-priced man? Vell, yes, I vas a high-priced man."

"Oh, you're aggravating me. Of course you want

$1.85 a day — every one wants it! You know perfectly well that that has very little to do with your being a high-priced man. For goodness' sake answer my questions, and don't waste any more of my time. Now come over here. You see that pile of pig iron?"

"Yes."

"You see that car?"

"Yes."

"Well, if you are a high-priced man, you will load that pig iron on that car to-morrow for $1.85. Now do wake up and answer my question. Tell me whether you are a high-priced man or not."

"Vell — did I got $1.85 for loading dot pig iron on dot car to-morrow?"

"Yes, of course you do, and you get $1.85 for loading a pile like that every day right through the year. That is what a high-priced man does, and you know it just as well as I do."

"Vell, dot's all right. I could load dot pig iron on the car to-morrow for $1.85, and I get it every day, don't I?"

"Certainly you do — certainly you do."

"Vell, den, I vas a high-priced man."

"Now, hold on, hold on. You know just as well as I do that a high-priced man has to do exactly as he's told from morning till night. You have seen this man here before, haven't you?"

"No, I never saw him."

"Well, if you are a high-priced man, you will do exactly as this man tells you to-morrow, from morning till night. When he tells you to pick up a pig and walk, you pick it up and you walk, and when he tells you to sit down and rest, you sit down. You do that right straight through the day. And what's more, no back talk. Now a high-priced man does just what he's told to do, and no back talk. Do you understand that? When this man tells you to walk, you walk; when he tells you to sit down, you sit down, and you don't talk back at him. Now you come on to work here to-morrow morning and I'll know before night whether you are really a high-priced man or not."

This seems to be rather rough talk. And indeed it would be if applied to an educated mechanic, or even an intelligent laborer. With a man of the mentally sluggish type of Schmidt it is appropriate and not unkind, since it is effective in fixing his attention on the high wages which he wants and away from what, if it were called to his attention, he probably would consider impossibly hard work.

What would Schmidt's answer be if he were talked to in a manner which is usual under the management of "initiative and incentive"? say, as follows:

"Now, Schmidt, you are a first-class pig-iron handler and know your business well. You have been handling at the rate of $12\frac{1}{2}$ tons per day. I have given considerable study to handling pig iron, and feel sure that you could do a much larger day's work than you have been doing. Now don't you think that if you really tried you could handle 47 tons of pig iron per day, instead of $12\frac{1}{2}$ tons?"

What do you think Schmidt's answer would be to this?

Schmidt started to work, and all day long, and at regular intervals, was told by the man who stood over him with a watch, "Now pick up a pig and walk. Now sit down and rest. Now walk — now rest," etc. He worked when he was told to work, and rested when he was told to rest, and at half-past five in the afternoon had his $47\frac{1}{2}$ tons loaded on the car. And he practically never failed to work at this pace and do the task that was set him during the three years that the writer was at Bethlehem. And throughout this time he averaged a little more than $1.85 per day, whereas before he had never received over $1.15 per day, which was the ruling rate of wages at that time in Bethlehem. That is, he received 60 per cent. higher wages than were paid to other men who were not working on task work. One man after another was picked out and trained to handle pig iron at the rate of $47\frac{1}{2}$ tons per day until all of the pig iron was handled at this rate, and the men were receiving 60 per cent. more wages than other workmen around them.

The writer has given above a brief description of three of the four elements which constitute the essence of scientific management: first, the careful selection of the workman, and, second and third, the method of first inducing and then training and helping the workman to work according to the scientific method. Nothing has as yet been said about the science of handling pig iron. The writer trusts, however, that before leaving this illustration the reader will be thoroughly convinced that there is a science of handling pig iron, and further that this science amounts to so much that the man who is suited to handle pig iron cannot possibly understand it, nor even work in accordance with the laws of this science, without the help of those who are over him.

The writer came into the machine-shop of the Midvale Steel Company in 1878, after having served an apprenticeship as a pattern-maker and as a machinist. This was close to the end of the long period of depression following the panic of 1873, and business was so poor that it was impossible for many mechanics to get work at their trades. For this reason he was obliged to start as a day laborer instead of working as a mechanic. Fortunately for him, soon after he came into the shop the clerk of the shop was found stealing. There was no one else available, and so, having more education 'than the other laborers (since he had been prepared for college) he was given the position of clerk. Shortly after this he was given work as a machinist in running one of the lathes, and, as he turned out rather more work than other machinists were doing on similar lathes, after several months was made gang-boss over the lathes.

Almost all of the work of this shop had been done on piece work for several years. As was usual then, and in fact as is still usual in most of the shops in this country, the shop was really run by the workmen, and not by the bosses.   The workmen together had carefully planned just how fast each job should be done, and they had set a pace for each machine throughout the shop, which was limited to about one-third of a good day's work.   Every new workman who came into the shop was told at once by the other men exactly how much of each kind of work he was to do, and unless he obeyed these instructions he was sure before long to be driven out of the place by the men.

As soon as the writer was made gang-boss, one after another of the men came to him and talked somewhat as follows:

"Now, Fred, we're very glad to see that you've been made gang-boss.   You know the game all right, and we're sure that you're not likely to be a piecework hog.   You come along with us, and everything will be all right, but if you try breaking any of these rates you can be mighty sure that we'll throw you over the fence."

The writer told them plainly that he was now working on the side of the management, and that he proposed to do whatever he could to get a fair day's work out of the lathes.   This immediately started a war; in most cases a friendly war, because the men who were under him were his personal friends, but none the less a war, which as time went on grew more and more bitter.   The writer used every expedient to make them do a fair day's work, such as discharging or lowering the wages of the more stubborn men who refused to make any improvement, and such as lowering the piece-work price, hiring green men, and personally teaching them how to do the work, with the promise from them that when they had learned how, they would then do a fair day's work. While the men constantly brought such pressure to bear (both inside and outside the works) upon all those who started to increase their output that they were finally compelled to do about as the rest did, or else quit. No one who has not had this experience can have an idea of the bitterness which is gradually developed in such a struggle. In a war of this kind the workmen have one expedient which is usually effective. They use their ingenuity to contrive various ways in which the machines which they are running are broken or damaged — apparently by accident, or in the regular course of work — and this they always lay at the door of the foreman, who has forced them to drive the machine so hard that it is overstrained and is being ruined. And there are few foremen indeed who are able to stand up against the combined pressure of all of the men in the shop. In this case the problem was complicated by the fact that the shop ran both day and night.

The writer had two advantages, however, which are not possessed by the ordinary foreman, and these came, curiously enough, from the fact that he was not the son of a working man.

First, owing to the fact that he happened not to be of working parents, the owners of the company believed that he had the interest of the works more at heart than the other workmen, and they therefore had more confidence in his word than they did in that of the machinists who were under him. So that, when the machinists reported to the Superintendent that the machines were being smashed up because an incompetent foreman was overstraining them, the Superintendent accepted the word of the writer when he said that these men were deliberately breaking their machines as a part of the piece-work war which was going on, and he also allowed the writer to make the only effective answer to this Vandalism on the part of the men, namely: "There will be no more accidents to the machines in this shop. If any part of a machine is broken the man in charge of it must pay at least a. part of the cost of its repair, and the fines collected in this way will all be handed over to the mutual beneficial association to help care for sick workmen." This soon stopped the wilful breaking of machines.

Second. If the writer had been one of the workmen, and had lived where they lived, they would have brought such social pressure to bear upon him that it would have been impossible to have stood out against them. He would have been called "scab" and other foul names every time he appeared on the street, his wife would have been abused, and his children would have been stoned. Once or twice he was begged by some of his friends among the workmen not to walk home, about two and a half miles along the lonely path by the side of the railway. He was told that if he continued to do this it would be at the risk of his life. In all such cases, however, a display of timidity is apt to increase rather than diminish the risk, so the writer told these men to say to the other men in the shop that he proposed to walk home every night right up that railway track; that he never had carried and never would carry any weapon of any kind, and that they could shoot and be d——.

After about three years of this kind of struggling, the output of the machines had been materially increased, in many cases doubled, and as a result the writer had been promoted from one gang-boss-ship to another until he became foreman of the shop. For any right-minded man, however, this success is in no sense a recompense for the bitter relations which he is forced to maintain with all of those around him. Life which is one continuous struggle with other men is hardly worth living. His workman friends came to him continually and asked him, in a personal, friendly way, whether he would advise them, for their own best interest, to turn out more work. And, as a truthful man, he had to tell them that if he were in their place he would fight against turning out any more work, just as they were doing, because under the piece-work system they would be allowed to earn no more wages than they had been earning, and yet they would be made to work harder.

Soon after being made foreman, therefore, he decided to make a determined effort to in some way change the system of management, so that the interests of the workmen and the management should become the same, instead of antagonistic. This resulted, some three years later, in the starting of the type of management which is described in papers presented to the American Society of Mechanical Engineers entitled "A Piece-Rate System" and "Shop Management."

In preparation for this system the writer realized that the greatest obstacle to harmonious cooperation between the workmen and the management lay in the ignorance of the management as to what really constitutes a proper day's work for a workman. He fully realized that, although he was foreman of the shop, the combined knowledge and skill of the workmen who were under him was certainly ten times as great as his own. He therefore obtained the permission of Mr. William Sellers, who was at that time the President of the Midvale Steel Company, to spend some money in a careful, scientific study of the time required to do various kinds of work.

Mr. Sellers allowed this more as a reward for having, to a certain extent, "made good" as foreman of the shop in getting more work out of the men, than for any other reason. He stated, however, that he did not believe that any scientific study of this sort would give results of much value.

Among several investigations which were undertaken at this time, one was an attempt to find some rule, or law, which would enable a foreman to know in advance how much of any kind of heavy laboring work a man who was well suited to his job ought to do in a day; that is, to study the tiring effect of heavy labor upon a first-class man. Our first step was to employ a young college graduate to look up all that had been written on the subject in English, German, and French. Two classes of experiments had been made: one by physiologists who were studying the endurance of the human animal, and the other by engineers who wished to determine what fraction of a horse-power a man-power was. These experiments had been made largely upon men who were lifting loads by means of turning the crank of a winch from which weights were suspended, and others who were engaged in walking, running, and lifting weights in various ways. However, the records of these investigations were so meager that no law of any value could be deduced from them. We therefore started a series of experiments of our own.

Two first-class laborers were selected, men who had proved themselves to be physically powerful and who were also good steady workers. These men were paid double wages during the experiments, and were told that they must work to the best of their ability at all times, and that we should make certain tests with them from time to time to find whether they were "soldiering" or not, and that the moment either one of them started to try to deceive us he would be discharged. They worked to the best of their ability throughout the time that they were being observed.

Now it must be clearly understood that in these

experiments we were not trying to find the maximum work that a man could do on a short spurt or for a few days, but that our endeavor was to learn what really constituted a full day's work for a first-class man; the best day's work that a man could properly do, year in and year out, and still thrive under. These men were given all kinds of tasks, which were carried out each day under the close observation of the young college man who was conducting the experiments, and who at the same time noted with a stop-watch the proper time for all of the motions that were made by the men. Every element in any way connected with the work which we believed could have a bearing on the result was carefully studied and recorded. What we hoped ultimately to determine was what fraction of a horse-power a man was able to exert, that is, how many foot-pounds of work a man could do in a day.

After completing this series of experiments, therefore, each man's work for each day was translated into foot-pounds of energy, and to our surprise we found that there was no constant or uniform relation between the foot-pounds of energy which the man exerted during a day and the tiring effect of his work. On some kinds of work the man would be tired out when doing perhaps not more than one-eighth of a horse-power, while in others he would be tired to no greater extent by doing half a horse-power of work. We failed, therefore, to find any law which was an accurate guide to the maximum day's work for a first-class workman.

A large amount of very valuable data had been obtained, which enabled us to know, for many kinds of labor, what was a proper day's work. It did not seem wise, however, at this time to spend any more money in trying to find the exact law which we were after. Some years later, when more money was available for this purpose, a second series of experiments was made, similar to the first, but somewhat more thorough. This, however, resulted as the first experiments, in obtaining valuable information but not in the development of a law. Again, some years later, a third series of experiments was made, and this time no trouble was spared in our endeavor to make the work thorough. Every minute element which could in any way affect the problem was carefully noted and studied, and two college men devoted about three months to the experiments. After this data was again translated into foot-pounds of energy exerted for each man each day, it became perfectly clear that there is no direct relation between the horse-power which a man exerts (that is, his foot-pounds of energy per day) and the tiring effect of the work on the man. The writer, however, was quite as firmly convinced as ever that some definite, clear-cut law existed as to what constitutes a full day's work for a first-class laborer, and our data had been so carefully collected and recorded that he felt sure that the necessary information was included somewhere in the records. The problem of developing this law from the accumulated facts was therefore handed over to Mr. Carl G. Barth, who is a better mathematician than any of the rest of us, and we decided to investigate the problem in a new way, by graphically representing each element of the work through plotting curves, which should give us, as it were, a bird's-eye view of every element.   In a comparatively short time Mr. Barth had discovered the law governing the tiring effect of heavy labor on a first-class man.   And it is so simple in its nature that it is truly remarkable that it should not have been discovered and clearly understood years before.   The law which was developed is as follows:

The law is confined to that class of work in which the limit of a man's capacity is reached because he is tired out.   It is the law of heavy laboring, corresponding to the work of the cart horse, rather than that of the trotter.   Practically all such work consists of a heavy pull or a push on the man's arms, that is, the man's strength is exerted by either lifting or pushing something which he grasps in his hands.   And the law is that for each given pull or push on the man's arms it is possible for the workman to be under load for only a definite percentage of the day.   For example, when pig iron is being handled (each pig weighing 92 pounds), a first-class workman can only be under load 43 per cent. of the day.   He must be entirely free from load during 57 per cent. of the day.   And as the load becomes lighter, the percentage of the day under which the man can remain under load increases. So that, if the workman is handling a half-pig, weighing 46 pounds, he can then be under load 58 per cent. of the day, and only has to rest during 42 per cent. As the weight grows lighter the man can remain under load during a larger and larger percentage of the day, until finally a load is reached which he can carry in his hands all day long without being tired out. When that point has been arrived at this law ceases to be useful as a guide to a laborer's endurance, and some other law must be found which indicates the man's capacity for work.

When a laborer is carrying a piece of pig iron weighing 92 pounds in his hands, it tires him about as much to stand still under the load as it does to walk with it, since his arm muscles are under the same severe tension whether he is moving or not. A man, however, who stands still under a load is exerting no horse-power whatever, and this accounts for the fact that no constant relation could be traced in various kinds of heavy laboring work between the foot-pounds of energy exerted and the tiring effect of the work on the man. It will also be clear that in all work of this kind it is necessary for the arms of the workman to be completely free from load (that is, for the workman to rest) at frequent intervals. Throughout the time that the man is under a heavy load the tissues of his arm muscles are in process of degeneration, and frequent periods of rest are required in order that the blood may have a chance to restore these tissues to their normal condition.

To return now to our pig-iron handlers at the

Bethlehem Steel Company. If Schmidt had been allowed to attack the pile of 47 tons of pig iron without the guidance or direction of a man who understood the art, or science, of handling pig iron, in his desire to earn his high wages he would probably have tired himself out by 11 or 12 o'clock in the day. He would have kept so steadily at work that his muscles would not have had the proper periods of rest absolutely needed for recuperation, and he would have been completely exhausted early in the day. By having a man, however, who understood this law, stand over him and direct his work, day after day, until he acquired the habit of resting at proper intervals, he was able to work at an even gait all day long without unduly tiring himself.

Now one of the very first requirements for a man who is fit to handle pig iron as a regular occupation is that he shall be so stupid and so phlegmatic that he more nearly resembles in his mental make-up the ox than any other type. The man who is mentally alert and intelligent is for this very reason entirely unsuited to what would, for him, be the grinding monotony of work of this character. Therefore the workman who is best suited to handling pig iron is unable to understand the real science of doing this class of work. He is so stupid that the word "percentage" has no meaning to him, and he must consequently be trained by a man more intelligent than himself into the habit of working in accordance with the laws of this science before he can be successful.

The writer trusts that it is now clear that even in the case of the most elementary form of labor that is known, there is a science, and that when the man best suited to this class of work has been carefully selected, when the science of doing the work has been developed, and when the carefully selected man has been trained to work in accordance with this science, the results obtained must of necessity be overwhelmingly greater than those which are possible under the plan of "initiative and incentive."

Let us, however, again turn to the case of these pig-iron handlers, and see whether, under the ordinary type of management, it would not have been possible to obtain practically the same results.

The writer has put the problem before many good managers, and asked them whether, under premium work, piece work, or any of the ordinary plans of management, they would be likely even to approximate 47 tons [1] per man per day, and not a

[1] Many people have questioned the accuracy of the statement that first-class workmen can load 47½ tons of pig iron from the ground on to a car in a day. For those who are skeptical, therefore, the following data relating to this work are given:

First. That our experiments indicated the existence of the following law: that a first-class laborer, suited to such work as handling pig iron, could be under load only 42 per cent. of the day and must be free from load 58 per cent. of the day.

Second. That a man in loading pig iron from piles placed on the ground in an open field on to a car which stood on a track adjoining these piles, ought to handle (and that they did handle regularly) 47½ long tons (2240 pounds per ton) per day.

That the price paid for loading this pig iron was 3 9/10 cents per ton, and that the men working at it averaged $1.85 per day, whereas, in the past, they had been paid only $1.15 per day.

In addition to these facts, the following are given:

man has suggested that an output of over 18 to 25 tons could be attained by any of the ordinary expedients. It will be remembered that the Bethlehem men were loading only $12\frac{1}{2}$ tons per man. To go into the matter in more detail, however: As to the scientific selection of the men, it is a fact that in this gang of 75 pig-iron handlers only about one man in eight was physically capable of handling $47\frac{1}{2}$ tons per day. With the very best of intentions, the other seven out of eight men were physically unable to work at this pace. Now the one man in eight who was able to do this work was in no sense superior to the other men who were working on the

$47\frac{1}{2}$ long tons equal 106,400 pounds of pig iron per day.

At 92 pounds per pig, equals 1156 pigs per day.

42 per cent. of a day under load equals 600 minutes; multiplied by 0.42 equals 252 minutes under load.

252 minutes divided by 1156 pigs equals 0.22 minutes per pig under load.

A pig-iron handler walks on the level at the rate of one foot in 0.006 minutes. The average distance of the piles of pig iron from the car was 36 feet. It is a fact, however, that many of the pig-iron handlers ran with their pig as soon as they reached the inclined plank. Many of them also would run down the plank after loading the car. So that when the actual loading went on, many of them moved at a faster rate than is indicated by the above figures. Practically the men were made to take a rest, generally by sitting down, after loading ten to twenty pigs. This rest was in addition to the time which it took them to walk back from the car to the pile. It is likely that many of those who are skeptical about the possibility of loading this amount of pig iron do not realize that while these men were walking back they were entirely free from load, and that therefore their muscles had, during that time, the opportunity for recuperation. It will be noted that with an average distance of 36 feet of the pig iron from the car, these men walked about eight miles under load each day and eight miles free from load.

If any one who is interested in these figures will multiply them and divide them, one into the other, in various ways, he will find that all of the facts stated check up exactly.

gang. He merely happened to be a man of the type of the ox, — no rare specimen of humanity, difficult to find and therefore very highly prized. On the contrary, he was a man so stupid that he was unfitted to do most kinds of laboring work, even. The selection of the man, then, does not involve finding some extraordinary individual, but merely picking out from among very ordinary men the few who are especially suited to this type of work. Although in this particular gang only one man in eight was suited to doing the work, we had not the slightest difficulty in getting all the men who were needed — some of them from inside of the works and others from the neighboring country—who were exactly suited to the job.

Under the management of "initiative and incentive" the attitude of the management is that of "putting the work up to the workmen." What likelihood would there be, then, under the old type of management, of these men properly selecting themselves for pig-iron handling? Would they be likely to get rid of seven men out of eight from their own gang and retain only the eighth man? No! And no expedient could be devised which would make these men properly select themselves. Even if they fully realized the necessity of doing so in order to obtain high wages (and they are not sufficiently intelligent properly to grasp this necessity), the fact that their friends or their brothers who were working right alongside of them would temporarily be thrown out of a job because they were not suited to this kind of work would entirely prevent them from properly selecting themselves, that is, from removing the seven out of eight men on the gang who were unsuited to pig-iron handling.

As to the possibility, under the old type of management, of inducing these pig-iron handlers (after they had been properly selected) to work in accordance with the science of doing heavy laboring, namely, having proper scientifically determined periods of rest in close sequence to periods of work. As has been indicated before, the essential idea of the ordinary types of management is that each workman has become more skilled in his own trade than it is possible for any one in the management to be, and that, therefore, the details of how the work shall best be done must be left to him. The idea, then, of taking one man after another and training him under a competent teacher into new working habits until he continually and habitually works in accordance with scientific laws, which have been developed by some one else, is directly antagonistic to the old idea that each workman can best regulate his own way of doing the work. And besides this, the man suited to handling pig iron is too stupid properly to train himself. Thus it will be seen that with the ordinary types of management the development of scientific knowledge to replace rule of thumb, the scientific selection of the men, and inducing the men to work in accordance with these scientific principles are entirely out of the question. And this because the philosophy of the old management puts the entire responsibility upon the workmen, while the philosophy of the new places a great part of it upon the management.

With most readers great sympathy will be aroused because seven out of eight of these pig-iron handlers were thrown out of a job. This sympathy is entirely wasted, because almost all of them were immediately given other jobs with the Bethlehem Steel Company. And indeed it should be understood that the removal of these men from pig-iron handling, for which they were unfit, was really a kindness to themselves, because it was the first step toward finding them work for which they were peculiarly fitted, and at which, after receiving proper training, they could permanently and legitimately earn higher wages.

Although the reader may be convinced that there is a certain science back of the handling of pig iron, still it is more than likely that he is still skeptical as to the existence of a science for doing other kinds of laboring. One of the important objects of this paper is to convince its readers that every single act of every workman can be reduced to a science. With the hope of fully convincing the reader of this fact, therefore, the writer proposes to give several more simple illustrations from among the thousands which are at hand.

For example, the average man would question whether there is much of any science in the work of shoveling. Yet there is but little doubt, if any intelligent reader of this paper were deliberately to set out to find what may be called the foundation of the science of shoveling, that with perhaps 15 to 20 hours of thought and analysis he would be almost sure to have arrived at the essence of this science. On the other hand, so completely are the rule-of-thumb ideas still dominant that the writer has never met a single shovel contractor to whom it had ever even occurred that there was such a thing as the science of shoveling. This science is so elementary as to be almost self-evident.

For a first-class shoveler there is a given shovel load at which he will do his biggest day's work. What is this shovel load? Will a first-class man do more work per day with a shovel load of 5 pounds, 10 pounds, 15 pounds, 20, 25, 30, or 40 pounds? Now this is a question which can be answered only through carefully made experiments. By first selecting two or three first-class shovelers, and paying them extra wages for doing trustworthy work, and then gradually varying the shovel load and having all the conditions accompanying the work carefully observed for several weeks by men who were used to experimenting, it was found that a first-class man would do his biggest day's work with a shovel load of about 21 pounds. For instance, that this man would shovel a larger tonnage per day with a 21-pound load than with a 24-pound load or than with an 18-pound load on his shovel. It is, of course, evident that no shoveler can always take a load of exactly 21 pounds on his shovel, but nevertheless, although his load may vary 3 or 4 pounds one way or the other, either below or above the 21 pounds, he will do his biggest day's work when his average for the day is about 21 pounds.

The writer does not wish it to be understood that this is the whole of the art or science of shoveling. There are many other elements, which together go to make up this science. But he wishes to indicate the important effect which this one piece of scientific knowledge has upon the work of shoveling.

At the works of the Bethlehem Steel Company, for example, as a result of this law, instead of allowing each shoveler to select and own his own shovel, it became necessary to provide some 8 to 10 different kinds of shovels, etc., each one appropriate to handling a given type of material; not only so as to enable the men to handle an average load of 21 pounds, but also to adapt the shovel to several other requirements which become perfectly evident when this work is studied as a science. A large shovel tool room was built, in which were stored not only shovels but carefully designed and standardized labor implements of all kinds, such as picks, crowbars, etc. This made it possible to issue to each workman a shovel which would hold a load of 21 pounds of whatever class of material they were to handle: a small shovel for ore, say, or a large one for ashes. Iron ore is one of the heavy materials which are handled in a works of this kind, and rice coal, owing to the fact that it is so slippery on the shovel, is one of the lightest materials. And it was found on studying the rule-of-thumb plan at the Bethlehem Steel Company, where each shoveler owned his own shovel, that he would frequently go from shoveling ore, with a load of about 30 pounds per shovel, to handling rice coal, with a load on the same shovel of less than 4 pounds.   In the one case, he was so overloaded that it was impossible for him to do a full day's work, and in the other case he was so ridiculously underloaded that it was manifestly impossible to even approximate a day's work.

Briefly to illustrate some of the other elements which go to make up the science of shoveling, thousands of stop-watch observations were made to study just how quickly a laborer, provided in each case with the proper type of shovel, can push his shovel into the pile of materials and then draw it out properly loaded.   These observations were made first when pushing the shovel into the body of the pile.   Next when shoveling on a dirt bottom, that is, at the outside edge of the pile, and next with a wooden bottom, and finally with an iron bottom. Again a similar accurate time study was made of the time required to swing the shovel backward and then throw the load for a given horizontal distance, accompanied by a given height.   This time study was made for various combinations of distance and height.   With data of this sort before him, coupled with the law of endurance described in the case of the pig-iron handlers, it is evident that the man who is directing shovelers can first teach them the exact methods which should be employed to use their strength to the very best advantage, and can then assign them daily tasks which are so just that the workman can each day be sure of earning the large bonus which is paid whenever he successfully performs this task.

There were about 600 shovelers and laborers of this general class in the yard of the Bethlehem Steel Company at this time. These men were scattered in their work over a yard which was, roughly, about two miles long and half a mile wide. In order that each workman should be given his proper implement and his proper instructions for doing each new job, it was necessary to establish a detailed system for directing men in their work, in place of the old plan of handling them in large groups, or gangs, under a few yard foremen. As each workman came into the works in the morning, he took out of his own special pigeonhole, with his number on the outside, two pieces of paper, one of which stated just what implements he was to get from the tool room and where he was to start to work, and the second of which gave the history of his previous day's work; that is, a statement of the work which he had done, how much he had earned the day before, etc. Many of these men were foreigners and unable to read and write, but they all knew at a glance the essence of this report, because yellow paper showed the man that he had failed to do his full task the day before, and informed him that he had not earned as much as $1.85 a day, and that none but high-priced men would be allowed to stay permanently with this gang.   The hope was further expressed that he would earn his full wages on the following day.   So that whenever the men received white slips they knew that everything was all right, and whenever they received yellow slips they realized that they must do better or they would be shifted to some other class of work.

Dealing with every workman as a separate individual in this way involved the building of a labor office for the superintendent and clerks who were in charge of this section of the work.   In this office every laborer's work was planned out well in advance, and the workmen were all moved from place to place by the clerks with elaborate diagrams or maps of the yard before them, very much as chessmen are moved on a chess-board, a telephone and messenger system having been installed for this purpose.   In this way a large amount of the time lost through having too many men in one place and too few in another, and through waiting between jobs, was entirely eliminated.   Under the old system the workmen were kept day after day in comparatively large gangs, each under a single foreman, and the gang was apt to remain of pretty nearly the same size whether there was much or little of the particular kind of work on hand which this foreman had under his charge, since each gang had to be kept large enough to handle whatever work in its special line was likely to come along.

When one ceases to deal with men in large gangs or groups, and proceeds to study each workman as an individual, if the workman fails to do his task, some competent teacher should be sent to show him exactly how his work can best be done, to guide, help, and encourage him, and, at the same time, to study his possibilities as a workman. So that, under the plan which individualizes each workman, instead of brutally discharging the man or lowering his wages for failing to make good at once, he is given the time and the help required to make him proficient at his present job, or he is shifted to another class of work for which he is either mentally or physically better suited.

All of this requires the kindly cooperation of the management, and involves a much more elaborate organization and system than the old-fashioned herding of men in large gangs. This organization consisted, in this case, of one set of men, who were engaged in the development of the science of laboring through time study, such as has been described above; another set of men, mostly skilled laborers themselves, who were teachers, and who helped and guided the men in their work; another set of tool-room men who provided them with the proper implements and kept them in perfect order, and another set of clerks who planned the work well in advance, moved the men with the least loss of time from one place to another, and properly recorded each man's earnings, etc. And this furnishes an elementary illustration of what has been referred to as cooperation between the management and the workmen.

The question which naturally presents itself is whether an elaborate organization of this sort can be made to pay for itself; whether such an organization is not top-heavy. This question will best be answered by a statement of the results of the third year of working under this plan.

	Old Plan	New Plan Task Work
The number of yard laborers was reduced from between	400 & 600 down to about	140
Average number of tons per man per day	16	59
Average earnings per man per day	$1.15	$1.88
Average cost of handling a ton of 2240 lbs.	$0.072	$0.033

And in computing the low cost of $0.033 per ton, the office and tool-room expenses, and the wages of all labor superintendents, foremen, clerks, time-study men, etc., are included.

During this year the total saving of the new plan over the old amounted to $36,417.69, and during the six months following, when all of the work of the yard was on task work, the saving was at the rate of between $75,000 and $80,000 per year.

Perhaps the most important of all the results attained was the effect on the workmen themselves. A careful inquiry into the condition of these men developed the fact that out of the 140 workmen only two were said to be drinking men. This does not, of course, imply that many of them did not take an occasional drink. The fact is that a steady drinker would find it almost impossible to keep up with the pace which was set, so that they were practically all sober. Many, if not most of them, were saving money, and they all lived better than they had before. These men constituted the finest body of picked laborers that the writer has ever seen together, and they looked upon the men who were over them, their bosses and their teachers, as their very best friends; not as nigger drivers, forcing them to work extra hard for ordinary wages, but as friends who were teaching them and helping them to earn much higher wages than they had ever earned before. It would have been absolutely impossible for any one to have stirred up strife between these men and their employers. And this presents a very simple though effective illustration of what is meant by the words "prosperity for the employé, coupled with prosperity for the employer," the two principal objects of management. It is evident also that this result has been brought about by the application of the four fundamental principles of scientific management.

As another illustration of the value of a scientific study of the motives which influence workmen in their daily work, the loss of ambition and initiative will be cited, which takes place in workmen when they are herded into gangs instead of being treated as separate individuals. A careful analysis had demonstrated the fact that when workmen are herded together in gangs, each man in the gang becomes far less efficient than when his personal ambition is stimulated; that when men work in gangs, their individual efficiency falls almost invariably down to or below the level of the worst man in the gang; and that they are all pulled down instead of being elevated by being herded together. For this reason a general order had been issued in the Bethlehem Steel Works that not more than four men were to be allowed to work in a labor gang without a special permit, signed by the General Superintendent of the works, this special permit to extend for one week only. It was arranged that as far as possible each laborer should be given a separate individual task. As there were about 5000 men at work in the establishment, the General Superintendent had so much to do that there was but little time left for signing these special permits.

After gang work had been by this means broken up, an unusually fine set of ore shovelers had been developed, through careful selection and individual, scientific training. Each of these men was given a separate car to unload each day, and his wages depended upon his own personal work. The man who unloaded the largest amount of ore was paid the highest wages, and an unusual opportunity came for demonstrating the importance of individualizing each workman. Much of this ore came from the Lake Superior region, and the same ore was delivered both in Pittsburg and in Bethlehem in exactly similar cars. There was a shortage of ore handlers in Pittsburg, and hearing of the fine gang of laborers that had been developed at Bethlehem, one of the Pittsburg steel works sent an agent to hire the

Bethlehem men. The Pittsburg men offered $4\frac{9}{10}$ cents a ton for unloading exactly the same ore, with the same shovels, from the same cars, that were unloaded in Bethlehem for $3\frac{2}{10}$ cents a ton. After carefully considering this situation, it was decided that it would be unwise to pay more than $3\frac{2}{10}$ cents per ton for unloading the Bethlehem cars, because, at this rate, the Bethlehem laborers were earning a little over $1.85 per man per day, and this price was 60 per cent. more than the ruling rate of wages around Bethlehem.

A long series of experiments, coupled with close observation, had demonstrated the fact that when workmen of this caliber are given a carefully measured task, which calls for a big day's work on their part, and that when in return for this extra effort they are paid wages up to 60 per cent. beyond the wages usually paid, that this increase in wages tends to make them not only more thrifty but better men in every way; that they live rather better, begin to save money, become more sober, and work more steadily. When, on the other hand, they receive much more than a 60 per cent. increase in wages, many of them will work irregularly and tend to become more or less shiftless, extravagant, and dissipated. Our experiments showed, in other words, that it does not do for most men to get rich too fast.

After deciding, for this reason, not to raise the wages of our ore handlers, these men were brought into the office one at a time, and talked to somewhat as follows:

"Now, Patrick, you have proved to us that you are a high-priced man.   You have been earning every day a little more than $1.85, and you are just the sort of man that we want to have in our ore-shoveling gang.   A man has come here from Pittsburg, who is offering $4\frac{9}{10}$ cents per ton for handling ore while we can pay only $3\frac{2}{10}$ cents per ton.   I think, therefore, that you had better apply to this man for a job.   Of course, you know we are very sorry to have you leave us, but you have proved yourself a high-priced man, and we are very glad to see you get this chance of earning more money.   Just remember, however, that at any time in the future, when you get out of a job, you can always come right back to us.   There will always be a job for a high-priced man like you in our gang here."

Almost all of the ore handlers took this advice, and went to Pittsburg, but in about six weeks most of them were again back in Bethlehem unloading ore at the old rate of $3\frac{2}{10}$ cents a ton.   The writer had the following talk with one of these men after he had returned:

"Patrick, what are you doing back here?   I thought we had gotten rid of you."

"Well, sir, I'll tell you how it was.   When we got out there Jimmy and I were put on to a car with eight other men.   We started to shovel the ore out just the same as we do here.   After about half an hour I saw a little devil alongside of me doing pretty near nothing, so I said to him, 'Why don't you go to work?   Unless we get the ore out

of this car we won't get any money on pay-day.'
He turned to me and said, 'Who in —— are you?'
'Well,' I said, 'that's none of your business'; and
the little devil stood up to me and said, 'You'll
be minding your own business, or I'll throw you off
this car!' 'Well, I could have spit on him and
drowned him, but the rest of the men put down their
shovels and looked as if they were going to back
him up; so I went round to Jimmy and said (so
that the whole gang could hear it), 'Now, Jimmy,
you and I will throw a shovelful whenever this little
devil throws one, and not another shovelful.' So
we watched him, and only shoveled when he shoveled.
— When pay-day came around, though, we had less
money than we got here at Bethlehem. After that
Jimmy and I went in to the boss, and asked him
for a car to ourselves, the same as we got at Bethlehem, but he told us to mind our own business. And
when another pay-day came around we had less
money than we got here at Bethlehem, so Jimmy
and I got the gang together and brought them all
back here to work again."

When working each man for himself, these men
were able to earn higher wages at $3\frac{2}{10}$ cents a ton
than they could earn when they were paid $4\frac{9}{10}$ cents
a ton on gang work; and this again shows the great
gain which results from working according to even
the most elementary of scientific principles. But
it also shows that in the application of the most
elementary principles it is necessary for the management to do their share of the work in cooperating

with the workmen. The Pittsburg managers knew just how the results had been attained at Bethlehem, but they were unwilling to go to the small trouble and expense required to plan ahead and assign a separate car to each shoveler, and then keep an individual record of each man's work, and pay him just what he had earned.

Bricklaying is one of the oldest of our trades. For hundreds of years there has been little or no improvement made in the implements and materials used in this trade, nor in fact in the method of laying bricks. In spite of the millions of men who have practised this trade, no great improvement has been evolved for many generations. Here, then, at least, one would expect to find but little gain possible through scientific analysis and study. Mr. Frank B. Gilbreth, a member of our Society, who had himself studied bricklaying in his youth, became interested in the principles of scientific management, and decided to apply them to the art of bricklaying. He made an intensely interesting analysis and study of each movement of the bricklayer, and one after another eliminated all unnecessary movements and substituted fast for slow motions. He experimented with every minute element which in any way affects the speed and the tiring of the bricklayer.

He developed the exact position which each of the feet of the bricklayer should occupy with relation to the wall, the mortar box, and the pile of bricks, and so made it unnecessary for him to take a step or two toward the pile of bricks and back again each time a brick is laid.

He studied the best height for the mortar box and brick pile, and then designed a scaffold, with a table on it, upon which all of the materials are placed, so as to keep the bricks, the mortar, the man, and the wall in their proper relative positions. These scaffolds are adjusted, as the wall grows in height, for all of the bricklayers by a laborer especially detailed for this purpose, and by this means the bricklayer is saved the exertion of stooping down to the level of his feet for each brick and each trowelful of mortar and then straightening up again. Think of the waste of effort that has gone on through all these years, with each bricklayer lowering his body, weighing, say, 150 pounds, down two feet and raising it up again every time a brick (weighing about 5 pounds) is laid in the wall! And this each bricklayer did about one thousand times a day.

As a result of further study, after the bricks are unloaded from the cars, and before bringing them to the bricklayer, they are carefully sorted by a laborer, and placed with their best edge up on a simple wooden frame, constructed so as to enable him to take hold of each brick in the quickest time and in the most advantageous position. In this way the bricklayer avoids either having to turn the brick over or end for end to examine it before laying it, and he saves, also, the time taken in deciding which is the best edge and end to place on the outside of the wall. In most cases, also, he saves the time taken in disentangling the brick from a disorderly pile on the scaffold. This "pack" of bricks (as Mr. Gilbreth calls his loaded wooden frames) is placed by the helper in its proper position on the adjustable scaffold close to the mortar box.

We have all been used to seeing bricklayers tap each brick after it is placed on its bed of mortar several times with the end of the handle of the trowel so as to secure the right thickness for the joint. Mr. Gilbreth found that by tempering the mortar just right, the bricks could be readily bedded to the proper depth by a downward pressure of the hand with which they are laid. He insisted that his mortar mixers should give special attention to tempering the mortar, and so save the time consumed in tapping the brick.

Through all of this minute study of the motions to be made by the bricklayer in laying bricks under standard conditions, Mr. Gilbreth has reduced his movements from eighteen motions per brick to five, and even in one case to as low as two motions per brick. He has given all of the details of this analysis to the profession in the chapter headed "Motion Study," of his book entitled "Bricklaying System," published by Myron C. Clerk Publishing Company, New York and Chicago; E. F. N. Spon, of London.

An analysis of the expedients used by Mr. Gilbreth in reducing the motions of his bricklayers from eighteen to five shows that this improvement has been made in three different ways:

First. He has entirely dispensed with certain movements which the bricklayers in the past believed were necessary, but which a careful study and trial on his part have shown to be useless.

Second. He has introduced simple apparatus, such as his adjustable scaffold and his packets for holding the bricks, by means of which, with a very small amount of cooperation from a cheap laborer, he entirely eliminates a lot of tiresome and time-consuming motions which are necessary for the bricklayer who lacks the scaffold and the packet.

Third. He teaches his bricklayers to make simple motions with both hands at the same time, where before they completed a motion with the right hand and followed it later with one from the left hand.

For example, Mr. Gilbreth teaches his bricklayer to pick up a brick in the left hand at the same instant that he takes a trowelful of mortar with the right hand. This work with two hands at the same time is, of course, made possible by substituting a deep mortar box for the old mortar board (on which the mortar spread out so thin that a step or two had to be taken to reach it) and then placing the mortar box and the brick pile close together, and at the proper height on his new scaffold.

These three kinds of improvements are typical of the ways in which needless motions can be entirely eliminated and quicker types of movements substituted for slow movements when scientific motion study, as Mr. Gilbreth calls his analysis, time study, as the writer has called similar work, are applied in any trade.

Most practical men would (knowing the opposition of almost all tradesmen to making any change in their methods and habits), however, be skeptical as to the possibility of actually achieving any large results from a study of this sort. Mr. Gilbreth reports that a few months ago, in a large brick building which he erected, he demonstrated on a commercial scale the great gain which is possible from practically applying his scientific study. With union bricklayers, in laying a factory wall, twelve inches thick, with two kinds of brick, faced and ruled joints on both sides of the wall, he averaged, after his selected workmen had become skilful in his new methods, 350 bricks per man *per hour;* whereas the average speed of doing this work with the old methods was, in that section of the country, 120 bricks per man per hour. His bricklayers were taught his new method of bricklaying by their foreman. Those who failed to profit by their teaching were dropped, and each man, as he became proficient under the new method, received a substantial (not a small) increase in his wages. With a view to individualizing his workmen and stimulating each man to do his best, Mr. Gilbreth also developed an ingenious method for measuring and recording the number of bricks laid by each man, and for telling each workman at frequent intervals how many bricks he had succeeded in laying.

It is only when this work is compared with the

conditions which prevail under the tyranny of some of our misguided bricklayers' unions that the great waste of human effort which is going on will be realized.   In one foreign city the bricklayers' union have restricted their men to *275 bricks per day* on work of this character when working for the city, and *375* per day when working for private owners.   The members of this union are probably sincere in their belief that this restriction of output is a benefit to their trade.   It should be plain to all men, however, that this deliberate loafing is almost criminal, in that it inevitably results in making every workman's family pay higher rent for their housing, and also in the end drives work and trade away from their city, instead of bringing it to it.

Why is it, in a trade which has been continually practised since before the Christian era, and with implements practically the same as they now are, that this simplification of the bricklayer's movements, this great gain, has not been made before?

It is highly likely that many times during all of these years individual bricklayers have recognized the possibility of eliminating each of these unnecessary motions.   But even if, in the past, he did invent each one of Mr. Gilbreth's improvements, no bricklayer could alone increase his speed through their adoption because it will be remembered that in all cases several bricklayers work together in a row and that the walls all around a building must grow at the same rate of speed.   No one bricklayer, then, can

work much faster than the one next to him.   Nor
has any one workman the authority to make other
men cooperate with him to do faster work.   It is
only through *enforced* standardization of methods,
enforced adoption of the best implements and working conditions, and *enforced* cooperation that this
faster work can be assured.   And the duty of enforcing the adoption of standards and of enforcing this
cooperation rests with the *management* alone.   The
management must supply continually one or more
teachers to show each new man the new and simpler
motions, and the slower men must be constantly
watched and helped until they have risen to their
proper speed.   All of those who, after proper teaching, either will not or cannot work in accordance
with the new methods and at the higher speed must
be discharged by the *management*.   The *management*
must also recognize the broad fact that workmen
will not submit to this more rigid standardization
and will not work extra hard, unless they receive
extra pay for doing it.

All of this involves an individual study of and
treatment for each man, while in the past they have
been handled in large groups.

The *management* must also see that those who
prepare the bricks and the mortar and adjust the
scaffold, etc., for the bricklayers, cooperate with
them by doing their work just right and always on
time; and they must also inform each bricklayer at
frequent intervals as to the progress he is making,
so that he may not unintentionally fall off in his

pace. Thus it will be seen that it is the assumption by the management of new duties and new kinds of work never done by employers in the past that makes this great improvement possible, and that, without this new help from the management, the workman even with full knowledge of the new methods and with the best of intentions could not attain these startling results.

Mr. Gilbreth's method of bricklaying furnishes a simple illustration of true and effective cooperation. Not the type of cooperation in which a mass of workmen on one side together cooperate with the management; but that in which several men in the management (each one in his own particular way) help each workman individually, on the one hand, by studying his needs and his shortcomings and teaching him better and quicker methods, and, on the other hand, by seeing that all other workmen with whom he comes in contact help and cooperate with him by doing their part of the work right and fast.

The writer has gone thus fully into Mr. Gilbreth's method in order that it may be perfectly clear that this increase in output and that this harmony could not have been attained under the management of "initiative and incentive" (that is, by putting the problem up to the workman and leaving him to solve it alone) which has been the philosophy of the past. And that his success has been due to the use of the four elements which constitute the essence of scientific management.

First. The development (by the management, not the workman) of the science of bricklaying, with rigid rules for each motion of every man, and the perfection and standardization of all implements and working conditions.

Second. The careful selection and subsequent training of the bricklayers into first-class men, and the elimination of all men who refuse to or are unable to adopt the best methods.

Third. Bringing the first-class bricklayer and the science of bricklaying together, through the constant help and watchfulness of the management, and through paying each man a large daily bonus for working fast and doing what he is told to do.

Fourth. An almost equal division of the work and responsibility between the workman and the management. All day long the management work almost side by side with the men, helping, encouraging, and smoothing the way for them, while in the past they stood one side, gave the men but little help, and threw on to them almost the entire responsibility as to methods, implements, speed, and harmonious cooperation.

Of these four elements, the first (the development of the science of bricklaying) is the most interesting and spectacular. Each of the three others is, however, quite as necessary for success.

It must not be forgotten that back of all this, and directing it, there must be the optimistic, determined, and hard-working leader who can wait patiently as well as work.

In most cases (particularly when the work to be done is intricate in its nature) the "development of the science" is the most important of the four great elements of the new management. There are instances, however, in which the "scientific selection of the workman" counts for more than anything else.

A case of this type is well illustrated in the very simple though unusual work of inspecting bicycle balls.

When the bicycle craze was at its height some years ago several million small balls made of hardened steel were used annually in bicycle bearings. And among the twenty or more operations used in making steel balls, perhaps the most important was that of inspecting them after final polishing so as to remove all fire-cracked or otherwise imperfect balls before boxing.

The writer was given the task of systematizing the largest bicycle ball factory in this country. This company had been running for from eight to ten years on ordinary day work before he undertook its reorganization, so that the one hundred and twenty or more girls who were inspecting the balls were "old hands" and skilled at their jobs.

It is impossible even in the most elementary work to change rapidly from the old independence of individual day work to scientific cooperation.

In most cases, however, there exist certain imperfections in working conditions which can at once be improved with benefit to all concerned.

In this instance it was found that the inspectors

(girls) were working ten and one-half hours per day (with a Saturday half holiday.)

Their work consisted briefly in placing a row of small polished steel balls on the back of the left hand, in the crease between two of the fingers pressed together, and while they were rolled over and over, they were minutely examined in a strong light, and with the aid of a magnet held in the right hand, the defective balls were picked out and thrown into especial boxes. Four kinds of defects were looked for — dented, soft, scratched, and fire-cracked — and they were mostly so minute as to be invisible to an eye not especially trained to this work. It required the closest attention and concentration, so that the nervous tension of the inspectors was considerable, in spite of the fact that they were comfortably seated and were not physically tired.

A most casual study made it evident that a very considerable part of the ten and one-half hours during which the girls were supposed to work was really spent in idleness because the working period was too long.

It is a matter of ordinary common sense to plan working hours so that the workers can really "work while they work" and "play while they play," and not mix the two.

Before the arrival of Mr. Sanford E. Thompson, who undertook a scientific study of the whole process, we decided, therefore, to shorten the working hours.

The old foreman who had been over the inspecting

room for years was instructed to interview one after another of the better inspectors and the more influential girls and persuade them that they could do just as much work in ten hours each day as they had been doing in ten and one-half hours. Each girl was told that the proposition was to shorten the day's work to ten hours and pay them the same day's pay they were receiving for the ten and one-half hours.

In about two weeks the foreman reported that all of the girls he had talked to agreed that they could do their present work just as well in ten hours as in ten and one-half and that they approved of the change.

The writer had not been especially noted for his tact so he decided that it would be wise for him to display a little more of this quality by having the girls vote on the new proposition. This decision was hardly justified, however, for when the vote was taken the girls were unanimous that $10\frac{1}{2}$ hours was good enough for them and they wanted no innovation of any kind.

This settled the matter for the time being. A few months later tact was thrown to the winds and the working hours were arbitrarily shortened in successive steps to 10 hours, $9\frac{1}{2}$, 9, and $8\frac{1}{2}$ (the pay per day remaining the same); and with each shortening of the working day the output increased instead of diminishing.

The change from the old to the scientific method in this department was made under the direction of Mr. Sanford E. Thompson, perhaps the most experienced man in motion and time study in this country, under the general superintendence of Mr. H. L. Gautt.

In the Physiological departments of our universities experiments are regularly conducted to determine what is known as the "personal coefficient" of the man tested. This is done by suddenly bringing some object, the letter A or B for instance, within the range of vision of the subject, who, the instant he recognizes the letter has to do some definite thing, such as to press a particular electric button. The time which elapses from the instant the letter comes in view until the subject presses the button is accurately recorded by a delicate scientific instrument.

This test shows conclusively that there is a great difference in the "personal coefficient" of different men. Some individuals are born with unusually quick powers of perception accompanied by quick responsive action. With some the message is almost instantly transmitted from the eye to the brain, and the brain equally quickly responds by sending the proper message to the hand.

Men of this type are said to have a low "personal coefficient," while those of slow perception and slow action have a *high* "personal coefficient."

Mr. Thompson soon recognized that the quality most needed for bicycle ball inspectors was a low "personal coefficient." Of course the ordinary qualities of endurance and industry were also called for.

For the ultimate good of the girls as well as the

company, however, it became necessary to exclude all girls who lacked a low "personal coefficient." And unfortunately this involved laying off many of the most intelligent, hardest working, and most trustworthy girls merely because they did not possess the quality of quick perception followed by quick action.

While the gradual selection of girls was going on other changes were also being made.

One of the dangers to be guarded against, when the pay of the man or woman is made in any way to depend on the quantity of the work done, is that in the effort to increase the quantity the quality is apt to deteriorate.

It is necessary in almost all cases, therefore, to take definite steps to insure against any falling off in quality before moving in any way towards an increase in quantity.

In the work of these particular girls quality was the very essence. They were engaged in picking out all defective balls.

The first step, therefore, was to make it impossible for them to slight their work without being found out. This was accomplished through what is known as over-inspection. Each one of four of the most trustworthy girls was given each day a lot of balls to inspect which had been examined the day before by one of the regular inspectors; the number identifying the lot to be over-inspected having been changed by the foreman so that none of the over-inspectors knew whose work they were examining. In addition to this one of the lots inspected by the four over-inspectors was examined on the following day by the chief inspector, selected on account of her especial accuracy and integrity.

An effective expedient was adopted for checking the honesty and accuracy of the over-inspection. Every two or three days a lot of balls was especially prepared by the foreman, who counted out a definite number of perfect balls, and added a recorded number of defective balls of each kind. Neither the inspectors nor the over-inspectors had any means of distinguishing this prepared lot from the regular commercial lots. And in this way all temptation to slight their work or make false returns was removed.

After insuring in this way against deterioration in quality, effective means were at once adopted to increase the output. Improved day work was substituted for the old slipshod method. An accurate daily record was kept both as to the quantity and quality of the work done in order to guard against any personal prejudice on the part of the foreman and to insure absolute impartiality and justice for each inspector. In a comparatively short time this record enabled the foreman to stir the ambition of all the inspectors by increasing the wages of those who turned out a large quantity and good quality, while at the same time lowering the pay of those who did indifferent work and discharging others who proved to be incorrigibly slow or careless. A careful examination was then made of the way in which each girl spent her time and an accurate time study was undertaken, through the use of a stop-watch and record blanks, to determine how fast each kind of inspection should be done, and to establish the exact conditions under which each girl could do her quickest and best work, while at the same time guarding against giving her a task so severe that there was danger from over fatigue or exhaustion. This investigation showed that the girls spent a considerable part of their time either in partial idleness, talking and half working, or in actually doing nothing.

Even when the hours of labor had been shortened from $10\frac{1}{2}$ to $8\frac{1}{2}$ hours, a close observation of the girls showed that after about an hour and one-half of consecutive work they began to get nervous. They evidently needed a rest. It is wise to stop short of the point at which overstrain begins, so we arranged for them to have a ten minutes period for recreation at the end of each hour and one quarter. During these recess periods (two of ten minutes each in the morning and two in the afternoon) they were obliged to stop work and were encouraged to leave their seats and get a complete change of occupation by walking around and talking, etc.

In one respect no doubt some people will say that these girls were brutally treated. They were seated so far apart that they could not conveniently talk while at work.

Shortening their hours of labor, however, and providing so far as we knew the most favorable working conditions made it possible for them to really work steadily instead of pretending to do so.

And it is only after this stage in the reorganization is reached, when the girls have been properly selected and on the one hand such precautions have been taken as to guard against the possibility of over-driving them, while, on the other hand, the temptation to slight their work has been removed and the most favorable working conditions have been established, that the final step should be taken which insures them what they most want, namely, *high wages*, and the employers what they most want, namely, the maximum output and best quality of work, — which means *a low labor cost*.

This step is to give each girl each day a carefully measured task which demands a full day's work from a competent operative, and also to give her a large premium or bonus whenever she accomplishes this task.

This was done in this case through establishing what is known as differential rate piece work.[1] Under this system the pay of each girl was increased in proportion to the quantity of her output and also still more in proportion to the accuracy of her work.

As will be shown later, the differential rate (the lots inspected by the over-inspectors forming the basis for the differential) resulted in a large gain in the quantity of work done and at the same time in a marked improvement in the quality.

Before they finally worked to the best advantage

[1] See paper read before the American Society of Mechanical Engineers, by Fred. W. Taylor, Vol. XVI, p. 856, entitled "Piece Rate System."

it was found to be necessary to measure the output of each girl as often as once every hour, and to send a teacher to each individual who was found to be falling behind to find what was wrong, to straighten her out, and to encourage and help her to catch up.

There is a general principle back of this which should be appreciated by all of those who are especially interested in the management of men.

A reward, if it is to be effective in stimulating men to do their best work, must come soon after the work has been done.   But few men are able to look forward for more than a week or perhaps at most a month, and work hard for a reward which they are to receive at the end of this time.

The average workman must be able to measure what he has accomplished and clearly see his reward at the end of each day if he is to do his best.   And more elementary characters, such as the young girls inspecting bicycle balls, or *children*, for instance, should have proper encouragement either in the shape of personal attention from those over them or an actual reward in sight as often as once an hour.

This is one of the principal reasons why cooperation or "profit-sharing" either through selling stock to the employés or through dividends on wages received at the end of the year, etc., have been at the best only mildly effective in stimulating men to work hard.   The nice time which they are sure to have to-day if they take things easily and go slowly proves more attractive than steady hard work with a possible reward to be shared with others six months later. A second reason for the inefficiency of profit-sharing schemes had been that no form of cooperation has yet been devised in which each individual is allowed free scope for his personal ambition. Personal ambition always has been and will remain a more powerful incentive to exertion than a desire for the general welfare. The few misplaced drones, who do the loafing and share equally in the profits, with the rest, under cooperation are sure to drag the better men down toward their level.

Other and formidable difficulties in the path of cooperative schemes are, the equitable division of the profits, and the fact that, while workmen are always ready to share the profits, they are neither able nor willing to share the losses. Further than this, in many cases, it is neither right nor just that they should share either the profits or the losses, since these may be due in great part to causes entirely beyond their influence or control, and to which they do not contribute.

To come back to the girls inspecting bicycle balls, however, the final outcome of all the changes was that *thirty-five girls did the work formerly done by one hundred and twenty*. And that the *accuracy of the work at the higher speed was two-thirds greater than at the former slow speed.*

The good that came to the girls was,

First. That they averaged from 80 to 100 per cent. higher wages than they formerly received.

Second. Their hours of labor were shortened from $10\frac{1}{2}$ to $8\frac{1}{2}$ per day, with a Saturday half holiday. And they were given four recreation periods properly distributed through the day, which made overworking impossible for a healthy girl.

Third. Each girl was made to feel that she was the object of especial care and interest on the part of the management, and that if anything went wrong with her she could always have a helper and teacher in the management to lean upon.

Fourth. All young women should be given two consecutive days of rest (with pay) each month, to be taken whenever they may choose. It is my impression that these girls were given this privilege, although I am not quite certain on this point.

The benefits which came to the company from these changes were:

First. A substantial improvement in the quality of the product.

Second. A material reduction in the cost of inspection, in spite of the extra expense involved in clerk work, teachers, time study, over-inspectors, and in paying higher wages.

Third. That the most friendly relations existed between the management and the employés, which rendered labor troubles of any kind or a strike impossible.

These good results were brought about by many changes which substituted favorable for unfavorable working conditions. It should be appreciated, however, that the one element which did more than all of the others was, the careful selection of girls with quick perception to replace those whose perceptions were slow — (the substitution of girls with a low personal coefficient for those whose personal coefficient was high) — the scientific selection of the workers.

The illustrations have thus far been purposely confined to the more elementary types of work, so that a very strong doubt must still remain as to whether this kind of cooperation is desirable in the case of more intelligent mechanics, that is, in the case of men who are more capable of generalization, and who would therefore be more likely, of their own volition, to choose the more scientific and better methods. The following illustrations will be given for the purpose of demonstrating the fact that in the higher classes of work the scientific laws which are developed are so intricate that the high-priced mechanic needs (even more than the cheap laborer) the cooperation of men better educated than himself in finding the laws, and then in selecting, developing, and training him to work in accordance with these laws. These illustrations should make perfectly clear our original proposition that in practically all of the mechanic arts the science which underlies each workman's act is so great and amounts to so much that the workman who is best suited to actually doing the work is incapable, either through lack of education or through insufficient mental capacity, of understanding this science.

A doubt, for instance, will remain in the minds perhaps of most readers (in the case of an establishment which manufactures the same machine, year in and year out, in large quantities, and in which, therefore, each mechanic repeats the same limited series of operations over and over again), whether the ingenuity of each workman and the help which he from time to time receives from his foreman will not develop such superior methods and such a personal dexterity that no scientific study which could be made would result in a material increase in efficiency.

A number of years ago a company employing about three hundred men, which had been manufacturing the same machine for ten to fifteen years, sent for us to report as to whether any gain could be made through the introduction of scientific management. Their shops had been run for many years under a good superintendent and with excellent foremen and workmen, on piece work. The whole establishment was, without doubt, in better physical condition than the average machine-shop in this country. The superintendent was distinctly displeased when told that through the adoption of task management the output, with the same number of men and machines, could be more than doubled. He said that he believed that any such statement was mere boasting, absolutely false, and instead of inspiring him with confidence, he was disgusted that any one should make such an impudent claim. He, however, readily assented to the proposition that he should select any one of the machines whose output he considered as representing the average of the shop, and that we should then demonstrate on this machine that through scientific methods its ouptut could be more than doubled.

The machine selected by him fairly represented the work of the shop. It had been run for ten or twelve years past by a first-class mechanic who was more than equal in his ability to the average workmen in the establishment. In a shop of this sort, in which similar machines are made over and over again, the work is necessarily greatly subdivided, so that no one man works upon more than a comparatively small number of parts during the year. A careful record was therefore made, in the presence of both parties, of the time actually taken in finishing each of the parts which this man worked upon. The total time required by him to finish each piece, as well as the exact speeds and feeds which he took, were noted, and a record was kept of the time which he took in setting the work in the machine and removing it. After obtaining in this way a statement of what represented a fair average of the work done in the shop, we applied to this one machine the principles of scientific management.

By means of four quite elaborate slide-rules, which have been especially made for the purpose of determining the all-round capacity of metal-cutting machines, a careful analysis was made of every element of this machine in its relation to the work in hand. Its pulling power at its various speeds, its feeding capacity, and its proper speeds were determined by means of the slide-rules, and changes were then made in the countershaft and driving pulleys so as to run it at its proper speed. Tools, made of high-speed steel, and of the proper shapes, were properly dressed, treated, and ground. (It should be understood, however, that in this case the high-speed steel which had heretofore been in general use in the shop was also used in our demonstration.) A large special slide-rule was then made, by means of which the exact speeds and feeds were indicated at which each kind of work could be done in the shortest possible time in this particular lathe. After preparing in this way so that the workman should work according to the new method, one after another, pieces of work were finished in the lathe, corresponding to the work which had been done in our preliminary trials, and the gain in time made through running the machine according to scientific principles ranged from two and one-half times the speed in the slowest instance to nine times the speed in the highest.

The change from rule-of-thumb management to scientific management involves, however, not only a study of what is the proper speed for doing the work and a remodeling of the tools and the implements in the shop, but also a complete change in the mental attitude of all the men in the shop toward their work and toward their employers. The physical improvements in the machines necessary to insure large gains, and the motion study followed by minute study with a stop-watch of the time in which each workman should do his work, can be made comparatively quickly. But the change in the mental attitude and in the habits of the three hundred or more workmen can be brought about only slowly and through a long series of object-lessons, which finally demonstrates to each man the great advantage which he will gain by heartily cooperating in his every-day work with the men in the management. Within three years, however, in this shop, the output had been more than doubled per man and per machine. The men had been carefully selected and in almost all cases promoted from a lower to a higher order of work, and so instructed by their teachers (the functional foremen) that they were able to earn higher wages than ever before. The average increase in the daily earnings of each man was about 35 per cent., while, at the same time, the sum total of the wages paid for doing a given amount of work was lower than before. This increase in the speed of doing the work, of course, involved a substitution of the quickest hand methods for the old independent rule-of-thumb methods, and an elaborate analysis of the hand work done by each man. (By hand work is meant such work as depends upon the manual dexterity and speed of a workman, and which is independent of the work done by the machine.) The time saved by scientific hand work was in many cases greater even than that saved in machine-work.

It seems important to fully explain the reason why, with the aid of a slide-rule, and after having studied the art of cutting metals, it was possible for the scientifically equipped man, who had never before seen these particular jobs, and who had never worked on this machine, to do work from two and one-half to nine times as fast as it had been done before by a good mechanic who had spent his whole time for some ten to twelve years in doing this very work upon this particular machine. In a word, this was possible because the art of cutting metals involves a true science of no small magnitude, a science, in fact, so intricate that it is impossible for any machinist who is suited to running a lathe year in and year out either to understand it or to work according to its laws without the help of men who have made this their specialty. Men who are unfamiliar with machine-shop work are prone to look upon the manufacture of each piece as a special problem, independent of any other kind of machine-work. They are apt to think, for instance, that the problems connected with making the parts of an engine require the especial study, one may say almost the life study, of a set of engine-making mechanics, and that these problems are entirely different from those which would be met with in machining lathe or planer parts. In fact, however, a study of those elements which are peculiar either to engine parts or to lathe parts is trifling, compared with the great study of the art, or science, of cutting metals, upon a knowledge of which rests the ability to do really fast machine-work of all kinds.

The real problem is how to remove chips fast from a casting or a forging, and how to make the piece smooth and true in the shortest time, and it matters but little whether the piece being worked upon is part, say, of a marine engine, a printing-press, or an automobile.   For this reason, the man with the slide-rule, familiar with the science of cutting metals, who had never before seen this particular work, was able completely to distance the skilled mechanic who had made the parts of this machine his specialty for years.

It is true that whenever intelligent and educated men find that the responsibility for making progress in any of the mechanic arts rests with them, instead of upon the workmen who are actually laboring at the trade, that they almost invariably start on the road which leads to the development of a science where, in the past, has existed mere traditional or rule-of-thumb knowledge.   When men, whose education has given them the habit of generalizing and everywhere looking for laws, find themselves confronted with a multitude of problems, such as exist in every trade and which have a general similarity one to another, it is inevitable that they should try to gather these problems into certain logical groups, and then search for some general laws or rules to guide them in their solution.   As has been pointed out, however, the underlying principles of the management of "initiative and incentive," that is, the underlying philosophy of this management, necessarily leaves the solution of all of these problems in the hands of each individual workman, while the philosophy of scientific management places their solution in the hands of the management.   The workman's whole time is each day taken in actually doing the work with his hands, so that, even if he had the necessary education and habits of generalizing in his thought, he lacks the time and the opportunity for developing these laws, because the study of even a simple law involving say time study requires the cooperation of two men, the one doing the work while the other times him with a stop-watch. And even if the workman were to develop laws where before existed only rule-of-thumb knowledge, his personal interest would lead him almost inevitably to keep his discoveries secret, so that he could, by means of this special knowledge, personally do more work than other men and so obtain higher wages.

Under scientific management, on the other hand, it becomes the duty and also the pleasure of those who are engaged in the management not only to develop laws to replace rule of thumb, but also to teach impartially all of the workmen who are under them the quickest ways of working. The useful results obtained from these laws are always so great that any company can well afford to pay for the time and the experiments needed to develop them. Thus under scientific management exact scientific knowledge and methods are everywhere, sooner or later, sure to replace rule of thumb, whereas under the old type of management working in accordance with scientific laws is an impossibility.

The development of the art or science of cutting metals is an apt illustration of this fact. In the fall of 1880, about the time that the writer started to make the experiments above referred to, to determine what constitutes a proper day's work for a laborer, he also obtained the permission of Mr. William Sellers, the President of the Midvale Steel Company, to make a series of experiments to determine what angles and shapes of tools were the best for cutting steel, and also to try to determine the proper cutting speed for steel. At the time that these experiments were started it was his belief that they would not last longer than six months, and, in fact, if it had been known that a longer period than this would be required, the permission to spend a considerable sum of money in making them would not have been forthcoming.

A 66-inch diameter vertical boring-mill was the first machine used in making these experiments, and large locomotive tires, made out of hard steel of uniform quality, were day after day cut up into chips in gradually learning how to make, shape, and use the cutting tools so that they would do faster work. At the end of six months sufficient practical information had been obtained to far more than repay the cost of materials and wages which had been expended in experimenting. And yet the comparatively small number of experiments which had been made served principally to make it clear that the actual knowledge attained was but a small fraction of that which still remained to be developed, and which was badly needed by us, in our daily attempt to direct and help the machinists in their tasks.

Experiments in this field were carried on, with

occasional interruption, through a period of about 26 years, in the course of which ten different experimental machines were especially fitted up to do this work. Between 30,000 and 50,000 experiments were carefully recorded, and many other experiments were made, of which no record was kept. In studying these laws more than 800,000 pounds of steel and iron was cut up into chips with the experimental tools, and it is estimated that from $150,000 to $200,000 was spent in the investigation.

Work of this character is intensely interesting to any one who has any love for scientific research. For the purpose of this paper, however, it should be fully appreciated that the motive power which kept these experiments going through many years, and which supplied the money and the opportunity for their accomplishment, was not an abstract search after scientific knowledge, but was the very practical fact that we lacked the exact information which was needed every day, in order to help our machinists to do their work in the best way and in the quickest time.

All of these experiments were made to enable us to answer correctly the two questions which face every machinist each time that he does a piece of work in a metal-cutting machine, such as a lathe, planer, drill press, or milling machine. These two questions are:

In order to do the work in the quickest time,

At what cutting speed shall I run my machine? and

What feed shall I use?

They sound so simple that they would appear

to call for merely the trained judgment of any good mechanic. In fact, however, after working 26 years, it has been found that the answer in every case involves the solution of an intricate mathematical problem, in which the effect of twelve independent variables must be determined.

Each of the twelve following variables has an important effect upon the answer. The figures which are given with each of the variables represent the effect of this element upon the cutting speed. For example, after the first variable (A) we quote, "The proportion is as 1 in the case of semi-hardened steel or chilled iron to 100 in the case of a very soft, low-carbon steel." The meaning of this quotation is that soft steel can be cut 100 times as fast as the hard steel or chilled iron. The ratios which are given, then, after each of these elements, indicate the wide range of judgment which practically every machinist has been called upon to exercise in the past in determining the best speed at which to run the machine and the best feed to use.

(A) The quality of the metal which is to be cut; i.e., its hardness or other qualities which affect the cutting speed. The proportion is as 1 in the case of semi-hardened steel or chilled iron to 100 in the case of very soft, low-carbon steel.

(B) The chemical composition of the steel from which the tool is made, and the heat treatment of the tool. The proportion is as 1 in tools made from tempered carbon steel to 7 in the best high-speed tools.

(C) The thickness of the shaving, or, the thickness of the spiral strip or band of metal which is to be removed by the tool. The proportion is as 1 with thickness of shaving $\frac{3}{16}$ of an inch to $3\frac{1}{2}$ with thickness of shaving $\frac{1}{64}$ of an inch.

(D) The shape or contour of the cutting edge of the tool. The proportion is as 1 in a thread tool to 6 in a broad-nosed cutting tool.

(E) Whether a copious stream of water or other cooling medium is used on the tool. The proportion is as 1 for tool running dry to 1.41 for tool cooled by a copious stream of water.

(F) The depth of the cut. The proportion is as 1 with $\frac{1}{2}$-inch depth of cut to 1.36 with $\frac{1}{8}$-inch depth of cut.

(G) The duration of the cut, i.e., the time which a tool must last under pressure of the shaving without being reground. The proportion is as 1 when tool is to be ground every $1\frac{1}{2}$ hours to 1.20 when tool is to be ground every 20 minutes.

(H) The lip and clearance angles of the tool. The proportion is as 1 with lip angle of 68 degrees to 1.023 with lip angle of 61 degrees.

(J) The elasticity of the work and of the tool on account of producing chatter. The proportion is as 1 with tool chattering to 1.15 with tool running smoothly.

(K) The diameter of the casting or forging which is being cut.

(L) The pressure of the chip or shaving upon the cutting surface of the tool.

(M) The pulling power and the speed and feed changes of the machine.

It may seem preposterous to many people that it should have required a period of 26 years to investigate the effect of these twelve variables upon the cutting speed of metals. To those, however, who have had personal experience as experimenters, it will be appreciated that the great difficulty of the problem lies in the fact that it contains so many variable elements. And in fact the great length of time consumed in making each single experiment was caused by the difficulty of holding eleven variables constant and uniform throughout the experiment, while the effect of the twelfth variable was being investigated. Holding the eleven variables constant was far more difficult than the investigation of the twelfth element.

As, one after another, the effect upon the cutting speed of each of these variables was investigated, in order that practical use could be made of this knowledge, it was necessary to find a mathematical formula which expressed in concise form the laws which had been obtained. As examples of the twelve formulæ which were developed, the three following are given:

$$P = 45{,}000 \; D^{\frac{11}{14}}F^{\frac{3}{4}}$$

$$V = \frac{90}{T^{\frac{1}{5}}}$$

$$V = \frac{11.9}{F^{0.665}\left(\dfrac{48}{3}D\right)^{0.2373 + \frac{2.4}{18 + 24D}}}$$

After these laws had been investigated and the various formulæ which mathematically expressed them had been determined, there still remained the difficult task of how to solve one of these complicated mathematical problems quickly enough to make this knowledge available for every-day use. If a good mathematician who had these formulæ before him were to attempt to get the proper answer (*i.e.*, to get the correct cutting speed and feed by working in the ordinary way) it would take him from two to six hours, say, to solve a single problem; far longer to solve the mathematical problem than would be taken in most cases by the workmen in doing the whole job in his machine. Thus a task of considerable magnitude which faced us was that of finding a quick solution of this problem, and as we made progress in its solution, the whole problem was from time to time presented by the writer to one after another of the noted mathematicians in this country. They were offered any reasonable fee for a rapid, practical method to be used in its solution. Some of these men merely glanced at it; others, for the sake of being courteous, kept it before them for some two or three weeks. They all gave us practically the same answer: that in many cases it was possible to solve mathematical problems which contained four variables, and in some cases problems with five or six variables, but that it was manifestly impossible to solve a problem containing twelve variables in any other way than by the slow process of "trial and error."

A quick solution was, however, so much of a necessity in our every-day work of running machine-shops, that in spite of the small encouragement received from the mathematicians, we continued at irregular periods, through a term of fifteen years, to give a large amount of time searching for a simple solution. Four or five men at various periods gave practically their whole time to this work, and finally, while we were at the Bethlehem Steel Company, the slide-rule was developed which is illustrated on Folder No. 11 of the paper "On the Art of Cutting Metals," and is described in detail in the paper presented by Mr. Carl G. Barth to the American Society of Mechanical Engineers, entitled "Slide-rules for the Machine-shop, as a part of the Taylor System of Management" (Vol. XXV of The Transactions of the American Society of Mechanical Engineers). By means of this slide-rule, one of these intricate problems can be solved in less than a half minute by any good mechanic, whether he understands anything about mathematics or not, thus making available for every-day, practical use the years of experimenting on the art of cutting metals.

This is a good illustration of the fact that some way can always be found of making practical, every-day use of complicated scientific data, which appears to be beyond the experience and the range of the technical training of ordinary practical men. These slide-rules have been for years in constant daily use by machinists having no knowledge of mathematics.

A glance at the intricate mathematical formulæ (see page 109) which represent the laws of cutting metals should clearly show the reason why it is impossible for any machinist, without the aid of these laws, and who depends upon his personal experience, correctly to guess at the answer to the two questions,

What speed shall I use?

What feed shall I use?

even though he may repeat the same piece of work many times.

To return to the case of the machinist who had been working for ten to twelve years in machining the same pieces over and over again, there was but a remote chance in any of the various kinds of work which this man did that he should hit upon the one best method of doing each piece of work out of the hundreds of possible methods which lay before him. In considering this typical case, it must also be remembered that the metal-cutting machines throughout our machine-shops have practically all been speeded by their makers by guesswork, and without the knowledge obtained through a study of the art of cutting metals. In the machine-shops systematized by us we have found that there is not one machine in a hundred which is speeded by its makers at anywhere near the correct cutting speed. So that, in order to compete with the science of cutting metals, the machinist, before he could use proper speeds, would first have to put new pulleys on the counter-shaft of his machine, and also make in most cases changes in the shapes and treatment of his tools, etc. Many of these changes are matters entirely beyond his control, even if he knows what ought to be done.

If the reason is clear to the reader why the rule-of-thumb knowledge obtained by the machinist who is engaged on *repeat work* cannot possibly compete with the true science of cutting metals, it should be even more apparent why the high-class mechanic, who is called upon to do a *great variety* of work from day to day, is even less able to compete with this science. The high-class mechanic who does a different kind of work each day, in order to do each job in the quickest time, would need, in addition to a thorough knowledge of the art of cutting metals, a vast knowledge and experience in the quickest way of doing each kind of hand work. And the reader, by calling to mind the gain which was made by Mr. Gilbreth through his motion and time study in laying bricks, will appreciate the great possibilities for quicker methods of doing all kinds of hand work which lie before every tradesman after he has the help which comes from a scientific motion and time study of his work.

For nearly thirty years past, time-study men connected with the management of machine-shops have been devoting their whole time to a scientific motion study, followed by accurate time study, with a stop-watch, of all of the elements connected with the machinist's work. When, therefore, the teachers, who form one section of the management, and who are cooperating with the working men, are in possession both of the science of cutting metals and of the equally elaborate motion-study and time-study science connected with this work, it is not difficult to appreciate why even the highest class mechanic is unable to do his best work without constant daily assistance from his teachers. And if this fact has been made clear to the reader, one of the important objects in writing this paper will have been realized.

It is hoped that the illustrations which have been given make it apparent why scientific management must inevitably in all cases produce overwhelmingly greater results, both for the company and its employés, than can be obtained with the management of "initiative and incentive." And it should also be clear that these results have been attained, not through a marked superiority in the mechanism of one type of management over the mechanism of another, but rather through the substitution of one set of underlying principles for a totally different set of principles, — by the substitution of one philosophy for another philosophy in industrial management.

To repeat then throughout all of these illustrations, it will be seen that the useful results have hinged mainly upon (1) the substitution of a science for the individual judgment of the workman; (2) the scientific selection and development of the workman, after each man has been studied, taught, and trained, and one may say experimented with, instead of allowing the workmen to select themselves and develop in a haphazard way; and (3) the intimate cooperation of the management with the workmen, so that they together do the work in accordance with the scientific laws which have been developed, instead of leaving the solution of each problem in the hands of the individual workman. In applying these new principles, in place of the old individual effort of each workman, both sides share almost equally in the daily performance of each task, the management doing that part of the work for which they are best fitted, and the workmen the balance.

It is for the illustration of this philosophy that this paper has been written, but some of the elements involved in its general principles should be further discussed.

The development of a science sounds like a formidable undertaking, and in fact anything like a thorough study of a science such as that of cutting metals necessarily involves many years of work. The science of cutting metals, however, represents in its complication, and in the time required to develop it, almost an extreme case in the mechanic arts. Yet even in this very intricate science, within a few months after starting, enough knowledge had been obtained to much more than pay for the work of experimenting. This holds true in the case of practically all scientific development in the mechanic arts. The first laws developed for cutting metals were crude, and contained only a partial knowledge of the truth, yet this imperfect knowledge was vastly better than the utter lack of exact information or the very imperfect rule of thumb which existed before, and it enabled the workmen, with the help of the management, to do far quicker and better work.

For example, a very short time was needed to discover one or two types of tools which, though imperfect as compared with the shapes developed years afterward, were superior to all other shapes and kinds in common use. These tools were adopted as standard and made possible an immediate increase in the speed of every machinist who used them. These types were superseded in a comparatively short time by still other tools which remained standard until they in their turn made way for later improvements.[1]

The science which exists in most of the mechanic arts is, however, far simpler than the science of cutting metals. In almost all cases, in fact, the laws or rules which are developed are so simple that the average man would hardly dignify them with

---

[1] Time and again the experimenter in the mechanic arts will find himself face to face with the problem as to whether he had better make immediate practical use of the knowledge which he has attained, or wait until some positive finality in his conclusions has been reached. He recognizes clearly the fact that he has already made some definite progress, but sees the possibility (even the probability) of still further improvement. Each particular case must of course be independently considered, but the general conclusion we have reached is that in most instances it is wise to put one's conclusions as soon as possible to the rigid test of practical use. The one indispensable condition for such a test, however, is that the experimenter shall have full opportunity, coupled with sufficient authority, to insure a thorough and impartial trial. And this, owing to the almost universal prejudice in favor of the old, and to the suspicion of the new, is difficult to get.

the name of a science. In most trades, the science is developed through a comparatively simple analysis and time study of the movements required by the workmen to do some small part of his work, and this study is usually made by a man equipped merely with a stop-watch and a properly ruled notebook. Hundreds of these "time-study men" are now engaged in developing elementary scientific knowledge where before existed only rule of thumb. Even the motion study of Mr. Gilbreth in bricklaying (described on pages 77 to 84) involves a much more elaborate investigation than that which occurs in most cases. The general steps to be taken in developing a simple law of this class are as follows:

First. Find, say, 10 or 15 different men (preferably in as many separate establishments and different parts of the country) who are especially skilful in doing the particular work to be analyzed.

Second. Study the exact series of elementary operations or motions which each of these men uses in doing the work which is being investigated, as well as the implements each man uses.

Third. Study with a stop-watch the time required to make each of these elementary movements and then select the quickest way of doing each element of the work.

Fourth. Eliminate all false movements, slow movements, and useless movements.

Fifth. After doing away with all unnecessary movements, collect into one series the quickest and best movements as well as the best implements.

This one new method, involving that series of motions which can be made quickest and best, is then substituted in place of the ten or fifteen inferior series which were formerly in use. This best method becomes standard, and remains standard, to be taught first to the teachers (or functional foremen) and by them to every workman in the establishment until it is superseded by a quicker and better series of movements. In this simple way one element after another of the science is developed.

In the same way each type of implement used in a trade is studied. Under the philosophy of the management of "initiative and incentive" each workman is called upon to use his own best judgment, so as to do the work in the quickest time, and from this results in all cases a large variety in the shapes and types of implements which are used for any specific purpose. Scientific management requires, first, a careful investigation of each of the many modifications of the same implement, developed under rule of thumb; and second, after a time study has been made of the speed attainable with each of these implements, that the good points of several of them shall be united in a single standard implement, which will enable the workman to work faster and with greater ease than he could before. This one implement, then, is adopted as standard in place of the many different kinds before in use, and it remains standard for all workmen to use until superseded by an implement which has been shown, through motion and time study, to be still better.

With this explanation it will be seen that the development of a science to replace rule of thumb is in most cases by no means a formidable undertaking, and that it can be accomplished by ordinary, every-day men without any elaborate scientific training; but that, on the other hand, the successful use of even the simplest improvement of this kind calls for records, system, and cooperation where in. the past existed only individual effort.

There is another type of scientific investigation which has been referred to several times in this paper, and which should receive special attention, namely, the accurate study of the motives which influence men. At first it may appear that this is a matter for individual observation and judgment, and is not a proper subject for exact scientific experiments. It is true that the laws which result from experiments of this class, owing to the fact that the very complex organism — the human being — is being experimented with, are subject to a larger number of exceptions than is the case with laws relating to material things. And yet laws of this kind, which apply to a large majority of men, unquestionably exist, and when clearly defined are of great value as a guide in dealing with men. In developing these laws, accurate, carefully planned and executed experiments, extending through a term of years, have been made, similar in a general way to the experiments upon various other elements which have been referred to in this paper.

Perhaps the most important law belonging to this class, in its relation to scientific management, is the effect which the task idea has upon the efficiency of the workman. This, in fact, has become such an important element of the mechanism of scientific management, that by a great number of people scientific management has come to be known as "task management."

There is absolutely nothing new in the task idea. Each one of us will remember that in his own case this idea was applied with good results in his schoolboy days. No efficient teacher would think of giving a class of students an indefinite lesson to learn. Each day a definite, clear-cut task is set by the teacher before each scholar, stating that he must learn just so much of the subject; and it is only by this means that proper, systematic progress can be made by the students. The average boy would go very slowly if, instead of being given a task, he were told to do as much as he could. All of us are grown-up children, and it is equally true that the average workman will work with the greatest satisfaction, both to himself and to his employer, when he is given each day a definite task which he is to perform in a given time, and which constitutes a proper day's work for a good workman. This furnishes the workman with a clear-cut standard, by which he can throughout the day measure his own progress, and the accomplishment of which affords him the greatest satisfaction.

The writer has described in other papers a series of experiments made upon workmen, which have resulted in demonstrating the fact that it is impossible, through any long period of time, to get workmen to work much harder than the average men around them, unless they are assured a large and a permanent increase in their pay. This series of experiments, however, also proved that plenty of workmen can be found who are willing to work at their best speed, provided they are given this liberal increase in wages. The workman must, however, be fully assured that this increase beyond the average is to be permanent. Our experiments have shown that the exact percentage of increase required to make a workman work at his highest speed depends upon the kind of work which the man is doing.

It is absolutely necessary, then, when workmen are daily given a task which calls for a high rate of speed on their part, that they should also be insured the necessary high rate of pay whenever they are successful. This involves not only fixing for each man his daily task, but also paying him a large bonus, or premium, each time that he succeeds in doing his task in the given time. It is difficult to appreciate in full measure the help which the proper use of these two elements is to the workman in elevating him to the highest standard of efficiency and speed in his trade, and then keeping him there, unless one has seen first the old plan and afterward the new tried upon the same man. And in fact until one has seen similar accurate experiments made upon various grades of workmen engaged in doing widely different types of work. The remarkable and almost uniformly good results from the *correct* application of the task and the bonus must be seen to be appreciated.

These two elements, the task and the bonus (which, as has been pointed out in previous papers, can be applied in several ways), constitute two of the most important elements of the mechanism of scientific management. They are especially important from the fact that they are, as it were, a climax, demanding before they can be used almost all of the other elements of the mechanism; such as a planning department, accurate time study, standardization of methods and implements, a routing system, the training of functional foremen or teachers, and in many cases instruction cards, slide-rules, etc. (Referred to later in rather more detail on page 129.)

The necessity for systematically teaching workmen how to work to the best advantage has been several times referred to. It seems desirable, therefore, to explain in rather more detail how this teaching is done. In the case of a machine-shop which is managed under the modern system, detailed written instructions as to the best way of doing each piece of work are prepared in advance, by men in the planning department. These instructions represent the combined work of several men in the planning room, each of whom has his own specialty, or function.   One of them, for instance, is a specialist on the proper speeds and cutting tools to be used.   He uses the slide-rules which have been above described as an aid, to guide him in obtaining proper speeds, etc.   Another man analyzes the best and quickest motions to be made by the workman in setting the work up in the machine and removing it, etc.   Still a third, through the time-study records which have been accumulated, makes out a time-table giving the proper speed for doing each element of the work.   The directions of all of these men, however, are written on a single instruction card, or sheet.

These men of necessity spend most of their time in the planning department, because they must be close to the records and data which they continually use in their work, and because this work requires the use of a desk and freedom from interruption.   Human nature is such, however, that many of the workmen, if left to themselves, would pay but little attention to their written instructions.   It is necessary, therefore, to provide teachers (called functional foremen) to see that the workmen both understand and carry out these written instructions.

Under functional management, the old-fashioned single foreman is superseded by eight different men, each one of whom has his own special duties, and these men, acting as the agents for the planning department (see paragraph 234 to 245 of the paper entitled "Shop Management"), are the expert teachers, who are at all times in the shop, helping and directing the workmen. Being each one chosen for his knowledge and personal skill in his specialty, they are able not only to tell the workman what he should do, but in case of necessity they do the work themselves in the presence of the workman, so as to show him not only the best but also the quickest methods.

One of these teachers (called the inspector) sees to it that he understands the drawings and instructions for doing the work. He teaches him how to do work of the right quality; how to make it fine and exact where it should be fine, and rough and quick where accuracy is not required, — the one being just as important for success as the other. The second teacher (the gang boss) shows him how to set up the job in his machine, and teaches him to make all of his personal motions in the quickest and best way. The third (the speed boss) sees that the machine is run at the best speed and that the proper tool is used in the particular way which will enable the machine to finish its product in the shortest possible time. In addition to the assistance given by these teachers, the workman receives orders and help from four other men; from the "repair boss" as to the adjustment, cleanliness, and general care of his machine, belting, etc.; from the "time clerk," as to everything relating to his pay and to proper written reports and returns; from the "route clerk," as to the order in which he does his work and as to the movement of the work from one part of the shop to another; and, in case a workman gets into any trouble with any of his various bosses, the "disciplinarian" interviews him.

It must be understood, of course, that all workmen engaged on the same kind of work do not require the same amount of individual teaching and attention from the functional foremen. The men who are new at a given operation naturally require far more teaching and watching than those who have been a long time at the same kind of jobs.

Now, when through all of this teaching and this minute instruction the work is apparently made so smooth and easy for the workman, the first impression is that this all tends to make him a mere automaton, a wooden man. As the workmen frequently say when they first come under this system, "Why, I am not allowed to think or move without some one interfering or doing it for me!" The same criticism and objection, however, can be raised against all other modern subdivision of labor. It does not follow, for example, that the modern surgeon is any more narrow or wooden a man than the early settler of this country. The frontiersman, however, had to be not only a surgeon, but also an architect, housebuilder, lumberman, farmer, soldier, and doctor, and he had to settle his law cases with a gun. You would hardly say that the life of the modern surgeon is any more narrowing, or that he is more of a wooden man than the frontiersman. The many problems to be met and solved by the surgeon are just as intricate and difficult and as developing and broadening in their way as were those of the frontiersman.

And it should be remembered that the training of the surgeon has been almost identical in type with the teaching and training which is given to the workman under scientific management. The surgeon, all through his early years, is under the closest supervision of more experienced men, who show him in the minutest way how each element of his work is best done. They provide him with the finest implements, each one of which has been the subject of special study and development, and then insist upon his using each of these implements in the very best way. All of this teaching, however, in no way narrows him. On the contrary he is quickly given the very best knowledge of his predecessors; and, provided (as he is, right from the start) with standard implements and methods which represent the best knowledge of the world up to date, he is able to use his own originality and ingenuity to make *real additions to the world's knowledge, instead of reinventing things which are old.* In a similar way the workman who is cooperating with his many teachers under scientific management has an opportunity to develop which is at least as good as and generally better than that which he had when the whole problem was "up to him" and he did his work entirely unaided.

If it were true that the workman would develop into a larger and finer man without all of this teaching, and without the help of the laws which have been formulated for doing his particular job, then it would follow that the young man who now comes to college to have the help of a teacher in mathematics, physics, chemistry, Latin, Greek, etc., would do better to study these things unaided and by himself. The only difference in the two cases is that students come to their teachers, while from the nature of the work done by the mechanic under scientific management, the teachers must go to him. What really happens is that, with the aid of the science which is invariably developed, and through the instructions from his teachers, each workman of a given intellectual capacity is enabled to do a much higher, more interesting, and finally more developing and more profitable kind of work than he was before able to do. The laborer who before was unable to do anything beyond, perhaps, shoveling and wheeling dirt from place to place, or carrying the work from one part of the shop to another, is in many cases taught to do the more elementary machinist's work, accompanied by the agreeable surroundings and the interesting variety and higher wages which go with the machinist's trade. The cheap machinist or helper, who before was able to run perhaps merely a drill press, is taught to do the more intricate and higher priced lathe and planer work, while the highly skilled and more intelligent machinists become functional foremen and teachers. And so on, right up the line.

It may seem that with scientific management there is not the same incentive for the workman to use his ingenuity in devising new and better methods of doing the work, as well as in improving his implements, that there is with the old type of management. It is true that with scientific management the workman is not allowed to use whatever implements and methods he sees fit in the daily practise of his work. Every encouragement, however, should be given him to suggest improvements, both in methods and in implements. And whenever a workman proposes an improvement, it should be the policy of the management to make a careful analysis of the new method, and if necessary conduct a series of experiments to determine accurately the relative merit of the new suggestion and of the old standard. And whenever the new method is found to be markedly superior to the old, it should be adopted as the standard for the whole establishment. The workman should be given the full credit for the improvement, and should be paid a cash premium as a reward for his ingenuity. In this way the true initiative of the workmen is better attained under scientific management than under the old individual plan.

The history of the development of scientific management up to date, however, calls for a word of warning. The mechanism of management must not be mistaken for its essence, or underlying philosophy. Precisely the same mechanism will in one case produce disastrous results and in another the most beneficent. The same mechanism which will produce the finest results when made to serve the underlying principles of scientific management, will lead to failure and disaster if accompanied by the wrong spirit in those who are using it. Hundreds of people have already mistaken the mechanism of this system for its essence. Messrs. Gantt, Barth, and the writer have presented papers to the American Society of Mechanical Engineers on the subject of scientific management. In these papers the mechanism which is used has been described at some length. As elements of this mechanism may be cited:

Time study, with the implements and methods for properly making it.

Functional or divided foremanship and its superiority to the old-fashioned single foreman.

The standardization of all tools and implements used in the trades, and also of the acts or movements of workmen for each class of work.

The desirability of a planning room or department.

The "exception principle" in management.

The use of slide-rules and similar time-saving implements.

Instruction cards for the workman.

The task idea in management, accompanied by a large bonus for the successful performance of the task.

The "differential rate."

Mnemonic systems for classifying manufactured products as well as implements used in manufacturing.

A routing system.

Modern cost system, etc., etc.

These are, however, merely the elements or details of the mechanism of management. Scientific management, in its essence, consists of a certain philosophy, which results, as before stated, in a combination of the four great underlying principles of management:[1]

When, however, the elements of this mechanism, such as time study, functional foremanship, etc., are used without being accompanied by the true philosophy of management, the results are in many cases disastrous. And, unfortunately, even when men who are thoroughly in sympathy with the principles of scientific management undertake to change too rapidly from the old type to the new, without heeding the warnings of those who have had years of experience in making this change, they frequently meet with serious troubles, and sometimes with strikes, followed by failure.

The writer, in his paper on "Shop Management," has called especial attention to the risks which managers run in attempting to change rapidly from the old to the new management. In many cases, however, this warning has not been heeded. The physical changes which are needed, the actual time study which has to be made, the standardization of all implements connected with the work,

[1] *First.* The development of a true science. *Second.* The scientific selection of the workman. *Third.* His scientific education and development. *Fourth.* Intimate friendly cooperation between the management and the men.

the necessity for individually studying each machine and placing it in perfect order, all take time, but the faster these elements of the work are studied and improved, the better for the undertaking.   On the other hand, the really great problem involved in a change from the management of "initiative and incentive" to scientific management consists in a complete revolution in the mental attitude and the habits of all of those engaged in the management, as well of the workmen.   And this change can be brought about only gradually and through the presentation of many object-lessons to the workman, which, together with the teaching which he receives, thoroughly convince him of the superiority of the new over the old way of doing the work.   This change in the mental attitude of the workman imperatively demands time.   It is impossible to hurry it beyond a certain speed.   The writer has over and over again warned those who contemplated making this change that it was a matter, even in a simple establishment, of from two to three years, and that in some cases it requires from four to five years.

The first few changes which affect the workmen should be made exceedingly slowly, and only one workman at a time should be dealt with at the start.   Until this single man has been thoroughly convinced that a great gain has come to him from the new method, no further change should be made. Then one man after another should be tactfully changed over.   After passing the point at which from one-fourth to one-third of the men in the employ of the company have been changed from the old to the new, very rapid progress can be made, because at about this time there is, generally, a complete revolution in the public opinion of the whole establishment and practically all of the workmen who are working under the old system become desirous to share in the benefits which they see have been received by those working under the new plan.

Inasmuch as the writer has personally retired from the business of introducing this system of management (that is, from all work done in return for any money compensation), he does not hesitate again to emphasize the fact that those companies are indeed fortunate who can secure the services of experts who have had the necessary practical experience in introducing scientific management, and who have made a special study of its principles. It is not enough that a man should have been a manager in an establishment which is run under the new principles. The man who undertakes to direct the steps to be taken in changing from the old to the new (particularly in any establishment doing elaborate work) must have had personal experience in overcoming the especial difficulties which are always met with, and which are peculiar to this period of transition. It is for this reason that the writer expects to devote the rest of his life chiefly to trying to help those who wish to take up this work as their profession, and to advising the managers and owners of companies in general as to the steps which they should take in making this change.

As a warning to those who contemplate adopting scientific management, the following instance is given.   Several men who lacked the extended experience which is required to change without danger of strikes, or without interference with the success of the business, from the management of "initiative and incentive" to scientific management, attempted rapidly to increase the output in quite an elaborate establishment, employing between three thousand and four thousand men.   Those who undertook to make this change were men of unusual ability, and were at the same time enthusiasts and I think had the interests of the workmen truly at heart.   They were, however, warned by the writer, before starting, that they must go exceedingly slowly, and that the work of making the change in this establishment could not be done in less than from three to five years.   This warning they entirely disregarded. They evidently believed that by using much of the mechanism of scientific management, in combination with the principles of the management of "initiative and incentive," instead of with the principles of scientific management, that they could do, in a year or two, what had been proved in the past to require at least double this time.   The knowledge obtained from accurate time study, for example, is a powerful implement, and can be used, in one case to promote harmony between the workmen and the management, by gradually educating, training, and leading the workmen into new and better methods of doing the work, or, in the other case, it may be used more or less as a club to drive the workmen into doing a larger day's work for approximately the same pay that they received in the past.   Unfortunately the men who had charge of this work did not take the time and the trouble required to train functional foremen, or teachers, who were fitted gradually to lead and educate the workmen.   They attempted, through the old-style foreman, armed with his new weapon (accurate time study), to drive the workmen, against their wishes, and without much increase in pay, to work much harder, instead of gradually teaching and leading them toward new methods, and convincing them through object-lessons that task management means for them somewhat harder work, but also far greater prosperity. The result of all this disregard of fundamental principles was a series of strikes, followed by the downfall of the men who attempted to make the change, and by a return to conditions throughout the establishment far worse than those which existed before the effort was made.

   This instance is cited as an object-lesson of the futility of using the mechanism of the new management while leaving out its essence, and also of trying to shorten a necessarily long operation in entire disregard of past experience.   It should be emphasized that the men who undertook this work were both able and earnest, and that failure was not due to lack of ability on their part, but to their undertaking to do the impossible. These particular men will not again make a similar mistake, and it is hoped that their experience may act as a warning to others.

In this connection, however, it is proper to again state that during the thirty years that we have been engaged in introducing scientific management there has not been a single strike from those who were working in accordance with its principles, even during the critical period when the change was being made from the old to the new. If proper methods are used by men who have had experience in this work, there is absolutely no danger from strikes or other troubles.

The writer would again insist that in no case should the managers of an establishment, the work of which is elaborate, undertake to change from the old to the new type unless the directors of the company fully understand and believe in the fundamental principles of scientific management and unless they appreciate all that is involved in making this change, particularly the time required, and unless they want scientific management greatly.

Doubtless some of those who are especially interested in working men will complain because under scientific management the workman, when he is shown how to do twice as much work as he formerly did, is not paid twice his former wages, while others who are more interested in the dividends than the workmen will complain that under this system the men receive much higher wages than they did before.

It does seem grossly unjust when the bare statement is made that the competent pig-iron handler, for instance, who has been so trained that he piles $3\frac{6}{10}$ times as much iron as the incompetent man formerly did, should receive an increase of only 60 per cent. in wages.

It is not fair, however, to form any final judgment until all of the elements in the case have been considered. At the first glance we see only two parties to the transaction, the workmen and their employers. We overlook the third great party, the whole people, — the consumers, who buy the product of the first two and who ultimately pay both the wages of the workmen and the profits of the employers.

The rights of the people are therefore greater than those of either employer or employé. And this third great party should be given its proper share of any gain. In fact, a glance at industrial history shows that in the end the whole people receive the greater part of the benefit coming from industrial improvements. In the past hundred years, for example, the greatest factor tending toward increasing the output, and thereby the prosperity of the civilized world, has been the introduction of machinery to replace hand labor. And without doubt the greatest gain through this change has come to the whole people — the consumer.

Through short periods, especially in the case of patented apparatus, the dividends of those who have introduced new machinery have been greatly increased, and in many cases, though unfortunately not universally, the employés have obtained materially higher wages, shorter hours, and better working conditions.   But in the end the major part of the gain has gone to the whole people.

And this result will follow the introduction of scientific management just as surely as it has the introduction of machinery.

To return to the case of the pig-iron handler.   We must assume, then, that the larger part of the gain which has come from his great increase in output will in the end go to the people in the form of cheaper pig-iron.   And before deciding upon how the balance is to be divided between the workmen and the employer, as to what is just and fair compensation for the man who does the piling and what should be left for the company as profit, we must look at the matter from all sides.

First.   As we have before stated, the pig-iron handler is not an extraordinary man difficult to find, he is merely a man more or less of the type of the ox, heavy both mentally and physically.

Second.   The work which this man does tires him no more than any healthy normal laborer is tired by a proper day's work.   (If this man is overtired by his work, then the task has been wrongly set and this is as far as possible from the object of scientific management.)

Third.   It was not due to this man's initiative or originality that he did his big day's work, but to the knowledge of the science of pig-iron handling developed and taught him by some one else.

Fourth. It is just and fair that men of the same general grade (when their all-round capacities are considered) should be paid about the same wages when they are all working to the best of their abilities. (It would be grossly unjust to other laborers, for instance, to pay this man $3\frac{6}{10}$ as high wages as other men of his general grade receive for an honest full day's work.)

Fifth. As is explained (page 74), the 60 per cent. increase in pay which he received was not the result of an arbitrary judgment of a foreman or superintendent, it was the result of a long series of careful experiments impartially made to determine what compensation is really for the man's true and best interest when all things are considered.

Thus we see that the pig-iron handler with his 60 per cent. increase in wages is not an object for pity but rather a subject for congratulation.

After all, however, facts are in many cases more convincing than opinions or theories, and it is a significant fact that those workmen who have come under this system during the past thirty years have invariably been satisfied with the increase in pay which they have received, while their employers have been equally pleased with their increase in dividends.

The writer is one of those who believes that more and more will the third party (the whole people), as it becomes acquainted with the true facts, insist that justice shall be done to all three parties. It will demand the largest efficiency from both employers and employés. It will no longer tolerate the type of employer who has his eye on dividends alone, who refuses to do his full share of the work and who merely cracks his whip over the heads of his workmen and attempts to drive them into harder work for low pay.   No more will it tolerate tyranny on the part of labor which demands one increase after another in pay and shorter hours while at the same time it becomes less instead of more efficient.

And the means which the writer firmly believes will be adopted to bring about, first, efficiency both in employer and employé and then an equitable division of the profits of their joint efforts will be scientific management, which has for its sole aim the attainment of justice for all three parties through impartial scientific investigation of all the elements of the problem.   For a time both sides will rebel against this advance.   The workers will resent any interference with their old rule-of-thumb methods, and the management will resent being asked to take on new duties and burdens; but in the end the people through enlightened public opinion will force the new order of things upon both employer and employé.

It will doubtless be claimed that in all that has been said no new fact has been brought to light that was not known to some one in the past.   Very likely this is true.   Scientific management does not necessarily involve any great invention, nor the discovery of new or startling facts.   It does, however, involve a certain *combination* of elements which have not existed in the past, namely, old knowledge so collected, analyzed, grouped, and classified into laws and rules that it constitutes a science; accompanied by a complete change in the mental attitude of the working men as well as of those on the side of the management, toward each other, and toward their respective duties and responsibilities. Also, a new division of the duties between the two sides and intimate, friendly cooperation to an extent that is impossible under the philosophy of the old management. And even all of this in many cases could not exist without the help of mechanisms which have been gradually developed.

It is no single element, but rather this whole combination, that constitutes scientific management, which may be summarized as:

Science, not rule of thumb.

Harmony, not discord.

Cooperation, not individualism.

Maximum output, in place of restricted output.

The development of each man to his greatest efficiency and prosperity.

The writer wishes to again state that: "The time is fast going by for the great personal or individual achievement of any one man standing alone and without the help of those around him. And the time is coming when all great things will be done by that type of cooperation in which each man performs the function for which he is best suited, each man preserves his own individuality and is supreme in his particular function, and each man at the same time loses none of his originality and proper personal initiative, and yet is controlled by and must work harmoniously with many other men."

The examples given above of the increase in output realized under the new management fairly represent the gain which is possible. They do not represent extraordinary or exceptional cases, and have been selected from among thousands of similar illustrations which might have been given.

Let us now examine the good which would follow the general adoption of these principles.

The larger profit would come to the whole world in general.

The greatest material gain which those of the present generation have over past generations has come from the fact that the average man in this generation, with a given expenditure of effort, is producing two times, three times, even four times as much of those things that are of use to man as it was possible for the average man in the past to produce. This increase in the productivity of human effort is, of course, due to many causes, besides the increase in the personal dexterity of the man. It is due to the discovery of steam and electricity, to the introduction of machinery, to inventions, great and small, and to the progress in science and education. But from whatever cause this increase in productivity has come, it is to the greater productivity of each individual that the *whole country* owes its greater prosperity.

Those who are afraid that a large increase in the productivity of each workman will throw other men out of work, should realize that the one element more than any other which differentiates civilized from uncivilized countries — prosperous from poverty-stricken peoples — is that the average man in the one is five or six times as productive as the other. It is also a fact that the chief cause for the large percentage of the unemployed in England (perhaps the most virile nation in the world), is that the workmen of England, more than in any other civilized country, are deliberately restricting their output because they are possessed by the fallacy that it is against their best interest for each man to work as hard as he can.

The general adoption of scientific management would readily in the future double the productivity of the average man engaged in industrial work. Think of what this means to the whole country. Think of the increase, both in the necessities and luxuries of life, which becomes available for the whole country, of the possibility of shortening the hours of labor when this is desirable, and of the increased opportunities for education, culture, and recreation which this implies. But while the whole world would profit by this increase in production, the manufacturer and the workman will be far more interested in the especial local gain that comes to them and to the people immediately around them. Scientific management will mean, for the employers and the workmen who adopt it — and particularly for those who adopt it first — the elimination of almost all causes for dispute and disagreement between them. What constitutes a fair day's work will be a question for scientific investigation, instead of a subject to be bargained and haggled over. Soldiering will cease because the object for soldiering will no longer exist. The great increase in wages which accompanies this type of management will largely eliminate the wage question as a source of dispute. But more than all other causes, the close, intimate cooperation, the constant personal contact between the two sides, will tend to diminish friction and discontent. It is difficult for two people whose interests are the same, and who work side by side in accomplishing the same object, all day long, to keep up a quarrel.

The low cost of production which accompanies a doubling of the output will enable the companies who adopt this management, particularly those who adopt it first, to compete far better than they were able to before, and this will so enlarge their markets that their men will have almost constant work even in dull times, and that they will earn larger profits at all times.

This means increase in prosperity and diminution in poverty, not only for their men but for the whole community immediately around them.

As one of the elements incident to this great gain in output, each workman has been systematically trained to his highest state of efficiency, and has been taught to do a higher class of work than he was able to do under the old types of management; and at the same time he has acquired a friendly mental attitude toward his employers and his whole working conditions, whereas before a considerable part of his time was spent in criticism, suspicious watchfulness, and sometimes in open warfare. This direct gain to all of those working under the system is without doubt the most important single element in the whole problem.

Is not the realization of results such as these of far more importance than the solution of most of the problems which are now agitating both the English and American peoples? And is it not the duty of those who are acquainted with these facts, to exert themselves to make the whole community realize this importance?

The author is constantly in receipt of letters asking for a list of the companies who are working under scientific management. It would be highly improper to furnish any one with a list of this kind. Many of those companies who have introduced scientific management would seriously object to answering the letters which would be showered upon them if such a list were given out. On the other hand, there are certain companies who are willing to take the trouble to answer such letters.

To all of those who are sufficiently interested in scientific management, the writer would most heartily extend an invitation to come to his house when they are in the neighborhood of Philadelphia. He will be glad to show them the details of scientific management as it is practised in several establishments in Philadelphia. Inasmuch as the greater part of the writer's time is given up to forwarding the cause of scientific management, he regards visits of this sort as a privilege, rather than as an intrusion.

000804 Quest 0000804A df
Set date:3/26/86 Rev. date: Alt. date:

OTHER WORKS BY THE GILBRETHS
IN
THE HIVE MANAGEMENT HISTORY SERIES

───────────

Frank B. Gilbreth

Bricklaying System
Concrete System
Field System
Motion Study
Motion Study For The Handicapped
Scientific Management Course

───────────

Frank & Lillian Gilbreth

Applied Motion Study
Fatigue Study

───────────

Lillian M. Gilbreth

The Psychology of Management
The Quest of The One Best Way

PRIMER

OF

SCIENTIFIC
MANAGEMENT

BY

FRANK B. GILBRETH

MEMBER AMERICAN SOCIETY OF MECHANICAL ENGINEERS
CONSULTING MANAGEMENT ENGINEER

WITH AN INTRODUCTION

BY

LOUIS D. BRANDEIS

SECOND EDITION

EASTON
HIVE PUBLISHING COMPANY
1985

Library of Congress Cataloging in Publication Data

Gilbreth, Frank Bunker, 1868–1924.
  Primer of scientific management.

      (Hive management history series, no. 12)
  "Facsimile reprint."
  Original t.p. has imprint: New York, D. Van Nostrand
Co., 1914.
  1. Industrial engineering. 2. Industrial management.
I. Title.
T55.9.G44   1914a   658.4   72-9513
ISBN 0-87960-024-1

PUBLISHERS' PREFACE

THE publishers of the *American Magazine* printed serially in their issues of March, April, and May, 1911, "The Principles of Scientific Management," by Frederick W. Taylor, M.E., Sc.D.

As a result, hundreds of letters came to them from their readers from all parts of the world, with requests for further information on the subject of the elimination of unnecessary waste in human effort.

These letters were all handed to Mr. Gilbreth to answer the questions they contained, and this book is the result.

The above fact explains, in part at least, why this book is not a complete treatise on Scientific Management.

Mr. Gilbreth's life work has been the elimination of unnecessary waste and fatigue in the operations of human labor. As a follower of Mr. Taylor, he has been able invariably to decrease labor costs and increase wages simultaneously.

The author will welcome any further questions from any interested reader which the present volume does not cover.

TABLE OF CONTENTS

CHAPTER IV

CHAPTER V

FOREWORD

In preparing this Primer of Scientific Management Mr. Gilbreth has performed a public service. His clear and simple instruction in the rudiments of the science will aid managers, superintendents, and foremen in their efforts to introduce it into their business. But the Primer will prove of greatest value in helping to remove from the minds of workingmen misapprehensions which have led some well-meaning labor leaders to oppose a movement from which labor has most to gain. That these labor leaders should, at the outset, have viewed the new management with suspicion was natural and proper. The "Beginning of Wisdom is Fear." But the second step in the path of wisdom is understanding; and courage should not lag far behind.

Scientific Management undertakes to secure greater production for the same or less effort. It secures to the workingman that development and rise in self-respect, that satisfaction with his work which in other lines of human activity accompanies achievement.

Eagerness and interest take the place of indifference, both because the workman is called upon to do the highest work of which he is capable, and also because in doing this better work he secures appropriate and substantial recognition and reward. Under Scientific Management men are led, not driven.   Instead of working unwillingly for their employer, they work in coöperation with the management for themselves and their employer on what is a "square deal."   If the fruits of Scientific Management are directed into the proper channels, the workingman will get not only a fair share, but a very large share, of the industrial profits arising from improved industry.

In order that the workingman may get this large share of the benefits through higher wages, shorter hours, regular employment, and better working conditions, the labor unions must welcome, not oppose, the introduction of Scientific Management to the end that the workingman through the unions may participate in fixing those wages, hours, and conditions.

Unless the workingman is so represented, there must be danger that his interests will not be properly cared for; and he cannot be properly represented except through organized labor.   The introduction of Scientific Management therefore offers to Organized Labor its greatest opportunity.

LOUIS D. BRANDEIS.

MAY, 1912.

CHAPTER I

SCIENTIFIC MANAGEMENT

What is scientific management?

Dr. Frederick W. Taylor says: —

"The art of management has been defined 'as knowing exactly what you want men to do and then seeing that they do it in the best and cheapest way' (Shop Management); also, 'The principal object of management should be to secure the maximum prosperity for the employer coupled with the maximum prosperity for each employee.'

"Scientific Management has for its very foundation the firm conviction that the true interests of the two are one and the same; that prosperity for the employer cannot exist through a long term of years unless it is accompanied by prosperity for the employee, and *vice versa;* and that it is possible to give the worker what he most wants — high wages — and the employer what he wants — a low labor cost — for his manufactures."

"Principles of Scientific Management." Harper and Brothers.

Mr. H. K. Hathaway says: —

"For its objects Scientific Management has the saving of energy, materials, and time, or in other words, the elimination of waste, and the increase of the world's wealth resulting from greater productivity of men and machinery. These it aims to achieve, in each industry to which it is applied, through bringing to bear upon each problem the analytical methods of investigation employed in the sciences; developing an art of science with well de-

1

fined and codified laws, in place of uncertain tradition and rule-of-thumb opinion. This is a broad statement of the first principle of Scientific Management."

Mr. James Mapes Dodge says in Paper 1115, Transactions of A. S. M. E., entitled "A History of the Introduction of a System of Shop Management": —

"The Taylor System is not a method of pay, a specific ruling of account books, nor the use of high-speed steel. It is simply an honest, intelligent effort to arrive at the absolute control in every department, to let tabulated and unimpeachable fact take the place of individual opinion; to develop 'team-play' to its highest possibility."

Col. Theodore Roosevelt says: —

"Scientific Management is the application of the conservation principle to production. It does not concern itself with the ownership of our natural resources. But in the factories where it is in force it guards these stores of raw materials from loss and misuse. First, by finding the right material — the special wood or steel or fiber — which is cheapest and best for the purpose. Second, by getting the utmost of finished product out of every pound or bale worked up. We couldn't ask more from a patriotic motive, than Scientific Management gives from a selfish one.

"Now, the time, health, and vitality of our people are as well worth conserving, at least, as our forests, minerals, and lands. And Scientific Management seems to do even more for the workman than for raw materials. It studies him at his task. Of the motions he makes and the efforts he puts forth, it determines by patient observation, which are the ones that get the result. It experiments to see whether these cannot be further shortened, or made easier for him.

"When the right way has been worked out in every detail, Scientific Management sets it up as a standard for that job; then instructs and trains the workman until he can accomplish this standard. And so on with all other workmen and all other jobs. The individual is first made efficient; his productive capacity is raised twenty-five or fifty per cent, sometimes doubled. From these efficient units is built up an efficiency organization. And when we get efficiency in all our industries and commercial ventures, national efficiency will be a fact."

Mr. Brandeis says in "Scientific Management and the Railroads," published by *Engineering Magazine*, New York: —

"Scientific Management means universal preparedness, the same kind of preparedness that secured to Prussia a victory over France and to Japan a victory over Russia. In Scientific Management nothing is left to chance; all is carefully planned in advance.

"Every operation is to be performed according to a predetermined schedule under definite instructions; and the execution under the plan is inspected and supervised at every point. Errors are prevented instead of being corrected. The terrible waste of delays and accidents is avoided. Calculation is substituted for guess; demonstration for opinion. The high efficiency of the limited passenger train is sought to be obtained in the ordinary operations of the business."

Professor Roe of Yale says that "Scientific Management" consists of three things: —

1. Accurate determination of the method and time in which a piece of work should be done.
2. Detailed instructions for 1.
3. Rewards and penalties to secure 1 and 2.

Mr. Cleveland Moffat says: —

"The basis of Scientific Management, as it is of art, is the rigorous cutting away of superfluities — not one wasted motion, not one wasted minute."

Engineering and Contracting says, in an editorial in the April 5, 1911, issue: —

"As we conceive it, Scientific Management consists in the conscious application of the laws inherent in the practice of successful managers and the laws of science in general. It has been called management engineering, which seems more fully to cover its general scope of the science."

Mr. Arthur W. Page says on page 14049 of *World's Work:* —

"What is 'Scientific Management'?

"Many people get the impression that Scientific Management consists of slide rules, instruction cards, eight sets of shovels, and the like.

"In reality the appliances are the least important part of it. The main thing is, first, to get the accurate information and, second, to continuously apply it."

Mr. H. L. Gantt says: —

"A system of management, to deserve the term 'scientific,' should aim to meet the following four conditions: —

"1. It should provide means for utilizing all of the available knowledge concerning the work in hand.

"2. It should provide means for seeing that the knowledge furnished is properly utilized.

"3. It should award liberal compensation for those who do use it properly.

"4. It should provide liberal means for acquiring new knowledge by scientific investigation, with adequate rewards for success.

"In introducing such a system, my advice is to begin at the bottom and go slowly."

W. B. Laine says: —

"Scientific Management is that form of Management which —

"(1) Separates an operation into its elements and determines—by study, observation, and experiment of unit times and motions—standards of equipment and method with definite instructions for operation; and

"(2) Determines a definite task difficult of attainment, but possible of daily and continuous performance with conservation of the physical and mental health of the worker; and

"(3) Routes material and effort in accordance with determined standards, providing instruction by functionally operating and trained teachers for the worker; and

"(4) Determines methods of payment, assuring a wage considerably above the ordinary and giving a large reward for attainment of the task and a definite loss for failure; and

"(5) By the elimination of waste material and effort, lost time, idle machinery, and capital, assures the maximum of prosperity for the employer and the employee."

TAYLOR SYSTEM

What is the difference between Scientific Management and the Taylor Plan?

Dr. Taylor's functional foreman plan of management founded upon time study is the *basis* for all scientific management, *i.e.* for types of management where scientific laboratory methods of analysis are substituted for the rule of "thumb methods" that have been handed down by word of mouth.

The Taylor plan of management is generally known as "Scientific Management," although there are many plans of management formulated by scientists that do not conform to the laws of management as discovered by Dr. Taylor.

Why is not Scientific Management called " the Taylor System "?

That type of management founded upon the best recognized scientific principles of to-day *should* be known as Taylor's plan of management, and *would* be, but for the personal objections of Dr. Taylor.

Where is Scientific Management best explained?

Dr. Taylor's writings describe his work in full.   See:—

Transactions of the American Society of Mechanical Engineers, Papers numbered—
  647. —"A Piece Rate System."   June, 1895.
  1003. —"Shop Management."   June, 1903.
  1119. —"On the Art of Cutting Metals."   December, 1906.

Also

American Magazine — March, April, May, 1911.
"The Principles of Scientific Management."   Harper's.
"Shop Management."   Harper's.

The value of Dr. Taylor's work was appreciated very early.

Mr. Harrington Emerson, industrial engineer, recognized the epoch-making value of A. S. M. E. Paper 1003 at the time of its presentation before the American Society of Mechanical Engineers, in 1903, when he said:—

"I regard the paper presented at this meeting by Mr. Taylor as the most important contribution ever presented to the Society, and one of the most important papers ever published in the United States."

TIME STUDY

What is " Time Study "?

Time study is the art of recording, analyzing, and synthesizing the time of the elements of any operation, usually a manual operation, but it has also been extended to mental and machinery operations.

It is one of the many remarkable inventions of Dr. Taylor while he was working at the Midvale Steel Works. It differs from the well-known process of timing the complete operation, as, for instance, the usual method for timing the athlete, in that the timing of time study is done on the elements of the process. Much ridiculous criticism has been put forward by well-meaning but uninformed persons, who claim that timing a worker down to a three hundredth of a minute is unkind, inhuman, and conducive to the worst form of slavery ever known. On the contrary, obtaining precise information regarding the smallest elements into which an art or a trade can be subdivided, and examining them separately, is the method adopted in all branches of scientific research.

For description of time study data by Mr. Sanford E. Thompson, C. E., see "Shop Management," Harper and Brothers.

For time study by Mr. R. T. Dana, see "Handbook of Steam Shovel Work," The Bucyrus Co.

MOTION STUDY

What is Motion Study?

Motion study is the science of eliminating wastefulness resulting from using unnecessary, ill-directed, and inefficient motions.

The aim of motion study is to find and perpetuate the scheme of least waste methods of labor.

By its use we have revolutionized several of the trades.[1] There is probably no art or trade that cannot have its output doubled by the application of the principles of motion study.   Among the variables affecting the motions most, are

VARIABLES OF THE WORKER

Anatomy	Experience	Nutrition
Brawn	Fatigue	Size
Contentment	Habits	Skill
Creed	Health	Temperament
Earning power	Mode of living	Training

VARIABLES OF THE SURROUNDINGS, EQUIPMENT, AND TOOLS

Appliances	Reward and punishment
Clothes	Size of unit moved
Colors	Special fatigue eliminating
Entertainment, music, reading, etc.	devices
	Surroundings
Heating, cooling, ventilating	Tools
Lighting	Union rules
Quality of material	Weight of unit moved

[1] "Motion Study," published by D. Van Nostrand Company, 25 Park Place, New York.

VARIABLES OF THE MOTION

Acceleration

Automaticity

Combination with other motions and sequence

Cost

Direction

Effectiveness

Foot pounds of work accomplished

Inertia and momentum overcome

Length

Necessity

Path

Play for position

Speed

Arthur Twining Hadley, President of Yale University, states in his book " Economics " : —

"The ability of a community to pay high wages seems to depend more upon the avoidance of waste than upon increase of accumulations."

TASK

What is meant by the word " task "?

The quantity of work of prescribed quality to be done in a given time, or the time required to do a certain quantity of output in a certain way as prophesied by scientific time study, is called the "task." The task is determined by building up synthetically the easiest, least fatiguing, least wasteful method, and allowing a definite percentage of time for rest, and a definite percentage for unavoidable delays. This percentage seldom amounts to less than 12½ per cent and often reaches to more than 30 per cent, and in some cases over 50 per cent.

The task is obviously, then, not a measure of how much a man can do under a short burst of speed, but instead is that maximum quantity that he can do day after day without speeding up and year after year with improvement to his health.

The task is the quantity that the man who is actually to do the work can do continuously and thrive.

FUNCTIONAL FOREMEN

What is the meaning of "Functional Foremen"?

Functional foremen differ from the usual type of foremen in that, while the latter have full charge of a certain number of men, the former have charge of a certain function in the handling of the men. For example, the principal functional foremen under the Taylor plan consist of

(*a*) Route clerk, and order of work clerk.

(*b*) Instruction card clerk.

(*c*) Time and cost clerk.

(*d*) Disciplinarian.

(*e*) Gang boss.

(*f*) Speed boss.

(*g*) Repair boss.

(*h*) Inspector.

All of these functional foremen must be specialists at their functions and must be prepared constantly to teach and help the individual workman with whom they work in direct contact.

The functional foreman under the scientific plan of management differs from the foreman under the traditional plan of management in that the latter has so many functions and duties to perform that he has to depend largely upon the individual workman to guess for himself as to which is the best way to do the work and to hold his job.

Regarding the savings and economic benefits accruing from the general principle of division of labor, Adam Smith said in 1776 (" An Inquiry into the Nature and Causes of the Wealth of Nations "): —

" This great increase in the quantity of work, which, in consequence of the division of labor, the same number of people are capable of performing, is owing to three different circumstances: first, to the increase of dexterity in every particular workman; secondly, to the saving of time which is commonly lost in passing from one species of work to another; and, lastly, to the invention of a great number of machines which facilitate and abridge labor, and enable one man to do the work of many."

Regarding division of mental labor, Charles Babbage said:—

" The effect of the *division of labor*, both mechanical and in mental operations, is, that it enables us to purchase and apply to each process precisely that quantity of skill and knowledge which is required for it; we avoid employing any part of the time of a man who can get eight or ten shillings a day by his skill in tempering needles, in turning a wheel, which can be done for sixpence a day; and we equally avoid the loss arising from an accomplished mathematician in performing the lowest processes of arithmetic."

CHAPTER II

TIME STUDY

What is the fundamental of Scientific Management?

The great fundamental of Scientific Management is time study.

On time study hangs the entire plan of the Taylor system of management. The apparently simple art of time study is in reality a great invention, for, previous to Taylor's discovery of it, there was no practical way of predetermining or prophesying accurately the amount of work that a man could do before he actually commenced to do it.

Any plan of management that does not include Taylor's plan of time study cannot be considered as highly efficient. We have never seen a case in our work where time study and analysis did not result in more than doubling the output of the worker. The greatest need to-day, as Dr. Taylor has already pointed out, is a handbook of time study data for assisting the workers to earn higher wages and the management to secure lower production costs. It is hoped that the day will soon arrive when the colleges will coöperate in undertaking this work in accordance with a definite plan, with a national bureau in charge of the entire work.

12

What are the purposes of Time Study?

The purposes of the scientific study of unit times are five, as follows: —

1. To obtain all the existing information about the art or trade being investigated that is possessed by the present masters, journeymen, and experts of that trade, who obtained the most of their information through the "journeyman to apprentice method" of teaching.

2. To get the most exact information regarding the time required to perform each smallest element of the operation, so that in building up the standard method synthetically the quickest elements and motions may be selected, in order that the workman can, other things being equal, use a method consisting of elements requiring the least time to perform.

3. To determine which motions and elements are the least fatiguing, that the worker may be caused no unnecessary fatigue in his work, nor any fatigue outside of his work of actually producing output.

4. To determine the amount of actual rest that each kind of work requires, that neither the management nor the man himself may injure the man by trying to make him do too much in order to obtain an increase over and above the unusually high wages offered by Scientific Management.

5. To determine the personal coefficient of each applicant for certain kinds of work, that he may be assisted in entering that vocation for which he is best fitted.

It will be seen by the above that it is necessary to obtain the most accurate and minute times if the greatest good to the worker and the management is to be obtained.

Why is the establishment of standards of tools, methods, and devices of such vital importance as a preliminary?

This is best answered by Mr. Morris Llewellyn Cooke, in his valuable "Report to the Carnegie Foundation For the Advancement of Teaching." He says (p. 6) : —

"A standard under modern Scientific Management is simply a carefully thought out method of performing a function, or carefully drawn specification covering an implement or some article of stores or of product. The idea of perfection is not involved in standardization. The standard method of doing anything is simply the best method that can be devised at the time the standard is drawn. Improvements in standards are wanted and adopted whenever and wherever they are found. There is absolutely nothing in standardization to preclude innovation. But to protect standards from changes which are not in the nature of improvements, certain safeguards are erected. These safeguards protect standards from change for the sake of change. All that is demanded under modern scientific management is that a proposed change in a standard must be scrutinized as carefully as the standard was scrutinized prior to its adoption; and further that this work be done by experts as competent to do it as were those who originally framed the standard. Standards adopted and protected in this way produce the best that is known at any one time. Standardization practiced in this way is a constant invitation to experimentation and improvement."

In what way can the general adoption of standards save money?

Dr. Taylor in his Paper 1003 ("Shop Management"), American Society of Mechanical Engineers, says : —

"284. It would seem almost unnecessary to dwell upon the desirability of standardizing, not only all of the tools, appliances, and implements throughout the works and office, but also the methods to be used in the multitude of small operations which are repeated day after day. There are many good managers of the old school, however, who feel that this standardization is not only unnecessary, but that it is undesirable, their principal reason being that it is better to allow each workman to develop his individuality by choosing the particular implements and methods which suit him best. And there is considerable weight in this contention when the scheme of management is to allow each workman to do the work as he pleases and hold him responsible for results. Unfortunately, in ninety-nine out of a hundred such cases only the first part of this plan is carried out. The workman chooses his own methods and implements, but is NOT HELD IN ANY STRICT SENSE ACCOUNTABLE unless the quality of the work is so poor or the quantity turned out is so small as to almost amount to a scandal. In the type of management advocated by the writer, this complete standardization of all details and methods is not only desirable, but absolutely indispensable as a preliminary to specifying the time in which each operation shall be done, and then insisting that it shall be done within the time allowed.

"285. Neglecting to take the time and trouble to thoroughly standardize all of such methods and details is one of the chief causes for setbacks and failure in introducing this system. Much better results can be attained, even if poor standards be adopted, than can be reached if some of a given class of implements are the best of their kind while others are poor. It is uniformity that is required. Better have them uniformly second class than mainly first with some second and some third class thrown in at random. In the latter case the workmen will almost always adopt the pace which conforms to the third class instead of the first or second. In fact, however, it is not a matter involving any great expense or time to select in each case standard implements which shall be nearly the best or the best of their kinds. The writer has never failed to make enormous gains in the economy of running by the adoption of standards.

"286. It was in the course of making a series of experiments with various air hardening tool steels with a view to adopting a standard for the Bethlehem works that Mr. White, together with the writer, discovered the Taylor-White process of treating tool steel, which marks a distinct improvement in the art; and the fact that this improvement was made, not by manufacturers of tool steel, but in the course of the adoption of standards, shows both the necessity and fruitfulness of methodical and careful investigation in the choice of much neglected details. The economy to be gained through the adoption of uniform standards is hardly realized at all by the managers of this country. No better illustration of this fact is needed than that of the present condition of the cutting tools used throughout the machine shops of the United States. Hardly a shop can be found in which tools made from a dozen different qualities of steel are not used side by side, in many cases with little or no means of telling one make from another; and, in addition, the shape of the cutting edge of the tool is in most cases left to the fancy of each individual workman. When one realizes that the cutting speed of the best treated air hardening steel is for a given depth of cut, feed, and quality of metal being cut, say sixty feet per minute, while with the same shaped tool made from the best carbon tool steel and with the same conditions, the cutting speed will be only twelve feet per minute, it becomes apparent how little the necessity for rigid standards is appreciated."

How can instruction cards be made out for laborers who cannot write or read any language, and who also cannot speak or understand the language of the management?

There are several ways of overcoming this difficulty. If the job is a long one of highly repetitive work, it is sometimes advisable to get an interpreter who can translate and teach the instruction card to the men. If the men read, it is possible to print the entire card in the two languages.

Where this has not been advisable, we have found that a full-sized exhibit of a complete unit to be constructed, maintained in all its various stages, and shown in detail as to method and result, has contained enough of the principles and features of the instruction card to serve the purpose.

We have found that stereoscopic (3-dimension) photographs and a stereoscope have been a great help, not only where the men do not understand the language of the management, but also in cases where they do.

Dr. Taylor says : —

"The instruction card can be put to wide and varied use. It is to the art of management what the drawing is to engineering, and, like the latter, should vary in size and form according to the amount and variety of the information which it is to convey. In some cases it should consist of a pencil memorandum on a small piece of paper which will be sent directly to the man requiring the instructions, while in others it will be in the form of several pages of typewritten matter, properly varnished and mounted, and issued under the check or other record system, so that it can be used time after time."

And any method or device that will enable the management to explain to the men exactly what is wanted, that they may do the performing exactly in accordance with the method required by the planning department, will perform the functions of the instruction card.

In whatever form or physical shape the instrument for conveying the information from the planning department is, one thing is certain, *i.e.* that the more explicit and definite this information, the better the results will be.

FUNCTIONAL FOREMEN

With so many functional foremen, who shall decide when they disagree?

Each functional foreman decides matters pertaining to his own work. In case of a disagreement, the disciplinarian decides as to questions of discipline and penalties.

On large works, where there are several foremen working at the same function, if they cannot agree immediately, the decision is left to their respective overforemen. If these, in turn, disagree, the question is referred to the assistant superintendent.

What is the advantage of a disciplinarian over a self-governing body?

The disciplinarian should be a trained specialist, who holds his job during good and efficient behavior. He should be free from the politics of election by a self-governing body. He should also be " of the management " in selecting employees, fixing base rates of wages, and determining promotion of deserving workers and foremen.

Don't the foremen have to spend too much of their time looking at papers instead of pushing the men?

The foremen in the planning department put their orders and teachings in writing on paper, defining clearly the standard method of doing the work.

The foremen of the performing department do not drive the men. Their duties are to explain the written orders of the planning department, and to see that they are carried out exactly as written.

Inasmuch as the papers show and describe the best-known method, it is essential that the foremen follow the instructions on the instruction card to the letter in order to obtain the best results.

How can a worker serve eight masters?

These eight so-called "masters" are functional foremen whose duties are to help the worker to do his work in the exact manner called for on the instruction card. Each man thus belongs to eight different gangs, or classes of instruction, and receives help from all eight teachers. "A man cannot serve two masters," but he can easily receive and accept help from eight teachers.

Mr. Wilfred Lewis, President of the Tabor Manufacturing Company, stated recently in an address on Scientific Management at the Congress of Technology, Boston, April 10, 1911, speaking of his own experience with the Taylor System: —

"Our wonderful increase in production is not due entirely to rapidity of performance, for in some instances very little gain in that direction has been made. A great deal is due to the functional foreman, whose duty it is to prepare and guide the way of every piece of work going through the shop.

"The old notion that a man cannot serve two masters or take orders from more than one superior is denied by the new philosophy, which makes it possible for a workman to have as many bosses as there are functions to be performed. There is no conflict of authority unless the functions overlap, and even there such conflict as may arise is salutary and to the interest of the company."

RATE OF COMPENSATION

How is it possible to pay high wages and at the same time have low costs of labor?

By finding the best way to do the work. This will enable the worker to produce much higher records of output at a lower unit cost, yet at a higher total daily wage, than he received under the old form of management. For example, suppose that under the old plan of management a man turned out about 10 pieces per day and received a total daily wage of $4.00. That would equal forty cents apiece.

Now suppose that by analyzing the method of making, down to the minutest motions, and by discovering a new method that took less time with less effort and was subject to less delay, the worker was able to put out 25 pieces, for which he received twenty-five cents apiece. The man's pay is here raised more than 56 per cent, and the production costs have been lowered 37½ per cent, out of which must be paid the cost of the investigation and of the planning department.

What are the essential differences between the different methods of payment and what are the good points and the failings of each?

(a) *Day Work.* — The most common method of payment of the worker, especially in establishments where but few men are employed, is the day work plan. Under this plan a man is paid for the time he works, and there is no agreement as to how much work he shall do in order to earn his day's pay.

Theoretically, this plan is very good, but in practice it is a great factor in decreasing efficiency, raising costs, reducing outputs, and, eventually, decreasing wages.

The day work system of payment would be an ideal method of payment of the workmen, from both the standpoint of the workers and the employers, if the employers could tell what rate per day would be the correct amount to pay each workman. But there is no way of determining that easily, consequently the men are paid by the position they hold and not for their individual merit, skill, or productivity. The workmen, seeing that their pay is determined by their class of trade, immediately recognize that it is useless to be particularly efficient because it will not affect their pay in the long run. Consequently all hands soon fall into that easy-going pace that is just fast enough to hold their job.

(b) *Old Bonus Scheme.* — The old scheme of paying a bonus has grown into disfavor generally because under it the amount of bonus was not determined scientifically; and, finally, it was used as a club over the heads of the workmen to drive them to greater efforts without adequate or just financial rewards. It also resulted in a poorer quality of finished output and oftentimes in accidents and injuries due to the generally careless methods resulting from the incentive to earn the extra financial reward.

(c) *Old-fashioned Piecework.* — Piecework would be an ideal method for paying the men if it were not for several facts not readily recognized as being of great injustice to the worker. First comes the difficulty of finding out the correct and just price that should be paid per piece.

Then there is the injustice to the worker while he is learning to do the work, also the fear on the part of the worker that the employer will cut the rate if he earns what the employer thinks is too much. Finally comes systematic soldiering, which is the worst thing in any type of management.

(d) *Gain Sharing.* — This method of compensating the workman was invented by Mr. Henry R. Towne in 1886. This method is fully described in the Transactions of the American Society of Mechanical Engineers, 1889, Paper 341.

(e) *Premium Plan.* — This method of paying workmen was invented by Mr. F. A. Halsey and is fully described in the Transactions of the American Society of Mechanical Engineers, 1891, Paper 499.

Mr. Taylor discusses these two methods of management (see Transactions of the American Society of Mechanical Engineers, 1895, Paper 647, ¶¶ 27–30).

(f) *Task with Bonus.* — This system was invented by Mr. H. L. Gantt. It consists of paying a regular day's pay to the worker in every case, even while he is learning and is unable to produce much output. It also provides for a scientifically determined task of standard quality, for the accomplishment of which the worker receives from 30 to 100 per cent extra wages. For any excess of output over and above the quantity of the task, the worker is paid at the same piece rate as is the rate a piece for the task. This is, therefore, a simple yet remarkable invention, for it insures a minimum of a full day's pay for the unskilled and the learners, and piecework for the skilled. (See "Work, Wages, and Profits," published by *The Engineering*

Magazine. See also Paper 928, Transactions of the American Society of Mechanical Engineers.)

(*g*) *Three-rate with Increased Rate.* — This system has many advantages in certain cases, and we have found it to be extremely valuable during the period of teaching the workmen how to achieve the task. It consists of —

(1) Paying a usual and customary day's pay to every worker, called the low rate.

(2) Paying a day's pay plus 10 per cent to a worker when he conforms to the exact method described upon the instruction card. This is called the middle rate and is used for the purpose of encouraging the worker and of inducing him to conform with great exactness to that method on which the unit times for work and percentage of time allowed for rest and unavoidable delays are based, and which has been determined by the planning department to be the best method that they have seen, heard of, or been able to devise by making a one best way from uniting best portions of many workers' methods. This middle rate is abandoned as soon as the worker has once achieved the task in the standard method. For the accomplishment of the task, which has been derived by scientific time study, an extra payment of from 30 to 100 per cent above the low rate. This is called the high rate, and for anything above the task a wage equal to the same piece rate for the increased quantity is paid. In some cases it is advisable to pay an increasing or differential rate for each piece when the number of pieces exceeds that of the task.

(*h*) *Differential Rate Piece.* — The Differential Rate Piece is an invention of Mr. Taylor, and, like everything he has done, is the most efficient of all methods of payment.

This method is undoubtedly the best method of compensating the worker. It gives unusually high pay for high outputs and unusually low pay for low outputs. It rewards the man who conforms to his instruction card so that he is most particular to coöperate with the management for the complete achievement of his task.

Paying an unusually low piece rate for failure to make obtainable output seems like a hardship on the worker; but it is absolutely necessary to penalize the lazy in this way because the "dependent sequences," as Mr. Harrington Emerson has described them, make it necessary to induce all men to work, by means of high pay for successful effort and low pay for lack of effort. In this way one worker, or class of workers, is not absolutely prevented from doing its work, which is dependent upon the preceding condition that the first workers achieve their tasks.

Example. — A bricklayer cannot achieve his task unless he is supplied with the brick, mortar, scaffold, and "line up" in the correct sequence at the right time, the right quantity, and of the right quality.

The mortar men cannot transport the mortar until it has been mixed. The mortar cannot be mixed until its ingredients have been received, etc.

While the Differential Rate Piece system is the most efficient, it should not be used until all the accompanying conditions for its success, including time study, the task, provision for proper inspection, methods and tools generally have been perfected and standardized.

While it is the most efficient, it requires a higher standard of management before it can be used to best advantage. It is particularly efficient on work that is repeated day after day and year after year.

It is hardly to be expected that any large establishment will ever have all employees working under one system of payment, therefore the system of payment must be selected according to the general condition of the management, whether or not work is sufficiently repetitive to warrant making entirely new time studies and instruction cards and many other factors controlling the situation.

Different methods of compensating workmen are explained particularly well in Chapter III of "Cost Keeping and Management Engineering," by Gillette and Dana.

It is necessary to say, further, that many ill-prepared antagonists to Scientific Management have stated frankly that they were "against any kind of a bonus scheme." It must be remembered, however, that "the method of payment is no more Scientific Management than a shingle is a roof," as Mr. Ernest Hamlin Abbott has so aptly stated.

Will not the use of different systems of payment make all kinds of confusion in an establishment?

No, on the contrary, the different conditions governing the work make it necessary to use several different forms of compensation to the workmen in order to secure the best results. In fact, the existence of a class of work on which the men are paid by the day provides one of the best forms of punishment for the use of the disciplinarian. After the men have gotten the high wages resulting from following the teachings provided for them, they dislike exceedingly to be put into the "day's pay" class. In the Link-Belt Co.'s works, — which are conceded to be of the most highly systematized, — there are at least four systems of payment, namely: —

(a) Day work,
(b) Piecework,
(c) Task with Bonus, and
(d) Differential Rate Piece.

The same is true with the Tabor Manufacturing Co., the Brighton Mills, Plimpton Press, Yale and Towne Manufacturing Co., and several works under the able management of Messrs. Dodge, Day and Zimmerman.

Why is not a coöperative plan better than Taylor's plan?

This question is best answered by quoting from Dr. Taylor's paper read before the A. S. M. E. in 1895, entitled a "Piece Rate System." We quote also pp. 73 to 77 inclusive of American Society of Mechanical Engineers, Paper 1003.

"73. Coöperation, or profit sharing, has entered the mind of every student of the subject as one of the possible and most attractive solutions of the problem; and there have been certain instances, both in England and France, of at least a partial success of coöperative experiments.

"74. So far as I know, however, these trials have been made either in small towns, remote from the manufacturing centers, or in industries which in many respects are not subject to ordinary manufacturing conditions.

" 75. Coöperative experiments have failed, and, I think, are generally destined to fail, for several reasons, the first and most important of which is, that no form of coöperation has yet been devised in which each individual is allowed free scope for his personal ambition. Personal ambition always has been and will remain a more powerful incentive to exertion than a desire for the general welfare. The few misplaced drones, who do the loafing and share equally in the profits with the rest, under coöperation are sure to drag the better men down toward their level.

" 76. The second and almost equally strong reason for failure lies in the remoteness of the reward. The average workman (I don't say all men) cannot look forward to a profit which is six months or a year away. The nice time which they are sure to have to-day, if they take things easily, proves more attractive than hard work, with a possible reward to be shared with others six months later.

" 77. Other and formidable difficulties in the path of coöperation are the equitable division of the profits, and the fact that, while workmen are always ready to share the profits, they are neither able nor willing to share the losses. Further than this, in many cases, it is neither right nor just that they should share either in the profits or the losses, since these may be due in great part to causes entirely beyond their influence or control, and to which they do not contribute."

Isn't it really the old piecework scheme under a new name with a few frills added?

In its final analysis, all compensation is more or less piecework. Even "day work" is a kind of piecework, *i.e.* the employer in effect says "I'll give you so much per day." Then if he thinks that he is not getting enough pieces done for the money, perhaps he does not say anything more, but simply sends the blue envelope to the worker.

Another employer might say, "I'll pay you 25 cents apiece," he and the employee both thinking that the latter could make anywhere from 8 to 16 pieces per day.   There is one great objection to this method that does not always show up immediately.   When it does, it does more damage than enough to offset all its value; namely, when, by special effort on the part of the employee, he makes say 32 pieces per day, and the employer, knowing that there are plenty of men to be had who would be delighted to work for $2.00 to $4.00 per day, cuts the rate.   As Dr. Taylor says, just two cuts of the rate for the same man, and he will then stop all planning except on the subject of how much output he can safely make without the fear of another cut.   It is surely not for the employee's interest to make any extra effort unless he is to be compensated for it.   This necessitates the setting of the piece rate scientifically and not by guess or arbitration or collective bargainings, and we say this emphatically, although we are thoroughly in favor of collective bargaining on many things, such, for example, as the minimum day's rate to be paid to the worker and the number of hours in the working day.

We will digress for a moment here and tell of an incident seen some years ago.   We had occasion to visit a factory, and saw a girl putting four-ounce lots of the factory's product into pasteboard boxes.   Her duties were simply to put exactly four ounces of merchandise into each pasteboard box and to put the cover on.   She was doing her work in a most inefficient way — obviously so.

Knowing that all the employees in that factory were on

piecework, we suggested to this girl that we could show her some economies of motions that would increase her output. She seemed much interested and watched our stop watch record an output several times greater our way than the way she had been working. She seemed delighted with the suggestion, and we were pleased to have shown her how she could do so many more dozen boxes per day. She followed the suggestion for about ten minutes, or until we walked away. When we came back, we saw that she was doing her work in the old way. We asked her why she did not do the work our way when it was so much more efficient. Her discouraged reply was, "What's the use; the boss here cuts the piece rate when any girl earns over $6.00 per week."

" Cannot the piece rate be cut under Scientific Management? "

Yes, and so can the throat of the goose that laid the golden eggs; but there are a great many incentives put upon the management not to cut the rate once it has been set. For example, for the best results the management must have established the reputation of never having cut a rate which has been set under Scientific Management. Then when a rate has been set and it has been found that no workman or gang boss teacher can teach the actual worker to do the work in the allotted time, the time allowed must be extended. On the other hand, if the time allowed is much longer than that required by the worker to accomplish his task, the management must stand by its mistake and take its medicine; but its medicine will not be bad for it at that. Such "candy work" can be used as a special prize for long service and special compensation for continuous merit.

The rate must not be set until the process and the method for executing the work have been completely changed. When the rate and the task and the method have been determined scientifically and not by rule of thumb, there will be no occasion or desire under Scientific Management to change the rate. We have seen cases where the earnings of the worker totaled to more than that of the gang bosses and, nevertheless, the unit costs were low.

What are the best remedies for soldiering?

There is but one remedy for soldiering, namely, an accurate knowledge on the part of the management of how much output constitutes a fair day's work, coupled with paying permanently unusually high wages, with no fear of a cut in rate.

CHAPTER III

FIELD OF APPLICABILITY

If Scientific Management is so worthy, why are there so few places organized under it at the present time?

Because there are so few engineers and teachers capable of installing it, and they are all busy with more work than they can do. Until some definite method is adopted for increasing the number of teachers, the progress will be slow.

Can Scientific Management be applied to office work, *i.e.* work that is mostly mental work?

Yes, there are many cases where it has been as effective as in the shop or on the job.

On work of repetitive character we have, in several instances, doubled the amount of output per clerk, and shortened the working hours.

We have never seen the case where higher wages, greater output, and lower costs have not resulted when an office force operated under Scientific Management.

What happens when a business is too small or too large to operate under exactly eight functional bosses?

If too small to warrant eight different functional foremen, fewer foremen can be used and each be given a number of functions to perform. If the job is too large for exactly eight men, then there may be several foremen to each function, with an "over foreman" to each group of foremen of the same function. Under the traditional form of management one foreman performs all eight functions as well as the time will permit.

For a description of practical application of Scientific Management, see a series of articles entitled "Applied Methods of Scientific Management," by Frederic A. Parkhurst, running in *Industrial Engineering* for 1911, and published in book form by Wiley & Co.

POSSIBILITY OF SUBSTITUTES FOR SCIENTIFIC MANAGEMENT

Why not get an extra good foreman and simply leave the question of management to him?

In the first place, "extra good foremen" are hard to find, and when found are more profitable to their employer and also themselves when acting in charge of that function for which they are specially fitted.

Furthermore, one man working alone cannot do such efficient work as can several specialists of less brilliancy, in team work, each at the function at which he is specially trained.

As Mr. Ernest Hamlin Abbott has said, in the *Outlook* for Jan. 7, 1911: —

"Scientific Management cannot be 'bought and delivered in a box,' but when it is once installed, it will bring results that cannot be achieved by a merely 'born manager.' If a man wants to practice medicine, it is well if he is a 'born doctor,' but nowadays it is not sufficient; it is not even necessary. So it will be with the manager."

Cannot the American workman devise efficient methods as well as the engineer?

As a proof that the workman cannot compete in devising efficient methods with the trained engineer, it is well to cite the paper 1010 of the Transactions of the American Society of Mechanical Engineers, by Mr. Carl G. Barth, entitled "Slide Rules for the Machine Shop as a part of the Taylor System of Management," in which he states : —

"Thus already during the first three weeks of the application of the slide rules to two lathes, the one a 27 inch, the other a 24 inch, in the larger of these shops, the output of these was increased to such an extent that they quite unexpectedly ran out of work on two different occasions, the consequence being that the superintendent, who had previously worried a good deal about how to get the great amount of work on hand for these lathes out of the way, suddenly found himself confronted with a real difficulty in keeping them supplied with work. But while the truth of this statement may appear quite incredible to a great many persons, to the writer himself, familiar and impressed as he has become with the great intricacy involved in the problem of determining the most economical way of running a machine tool, the application of a rigid mathematical solution to this problem as against the leaving it to the so-called practical judgment and experience of the operator, cannot otherwise result than in the exposure of the perfect folly of the latter method."

What is the reason that employees do not know how fast work should be done?

There are many reasons, such as —

(a) They have not investigated their problems by means of motion study and time study.

(b) They have not realized the importance of having each step in the dependent sequences carried out without delay.

(c) They have not been taught the saving in time caused by having all of the sequences obvious, and all of the planning and most of the brain work done by the planning department before the work is actually done.

(d) The workers have been taught, by the fear of running themselves out of a job or having their rate cut, that the safest plan for them is to soldier whenever possible.

(e) Lack of personal familiarity with stop watch records of elements of work of the best men, under standard conditions, is the cause of their lack of knowledge of how fast the work should be done.

Does not a good system of routing bring nearly all the benefits of Scientific Management?

A system of routing is but a small part of the entire plan of Scientific Management. It is a very necessary part, however, and the line determining just where routing leaves off and some of the other functions begin is arbitrary. One man has stated that even motion study is largely a matter of routing the various parts of the human body, particularly the hands, feet, eyes, and head.

For an illuminating discussion of routing and its relation to Scientific Management see "Industrial Plants," by Charles Day, published by *The Engineering Magazine*, 1911.

Is not loyalty and good will the thing that will make employees work most efficiently?

It is certainly a great factor in obtaining coöperation between the management and the workers. Scientific Management obtains good will by the square deal, by a division of the savings, by teaching, etc., while the old form of management sometimes endeavors to obtain it by jollying, "welfare work," picnics, self-governing committees, etc. The disadvantage of the last is that a self-governing committee does not get the best results, because it is not supplied with and does not know how best to use that data which has been obtained in a scientific manner.

PREPARATION FOR INTRODUCTION OF SCIENTIFIC MANAGEMENT

What preparation can be made for the advent of the Scientific Manager before he comes in?

There are many things that can be done. Among the most necessary and the easiest to do are four: —

(a) Establish standards of methods, and of tools everywhere.

(b) Install schedules and time tables.

(c) Place each man, as far as possible, so that his output and its unit cost shows up separately.

(d) Put present system in writing.

(See "Cost Keeping and Management Engineering," Gillette and Dana.)

These improvements will pay for themselves from the start and will facilitate the work of the efficiency engineer very materially.

PLACE OF INTRODUCTION OF SCIENTIFIC MANAGEMENT

Where is the best place to begin to install Scientific Management?

It should be first installed where it will have the least effect upon the workmen. When changes are to be made that affect the workmen, it is most desirable that those cases should be undertaken first that show most plainly that workmen are benefited and that show up clearest as an object lesson to all the workmen and to all the employers, superintendents, and foremen as to how Scientific Management simultaneously increases wages for the workers and cuts down production costs for the owner. It is desirable to start the installation in many places at the same time. Therefore the establishment of standards everywhere, including standard instruction cards for standard methods, motion study, time study, time cards, records of individual outputs, selecting and training the functional foremen, particularly the foreman in charge of the function of inspection, are the features that should be undertaken at the very first. Collect the great special knowledge that the functional foremen should possess and see that they learn it. In choosing which of two things is to be done first, always give precedence to that which can be nailed down and held from slipping back into the old rut, once it has been made to operate under the new Scientific Management.

METHOD OF INTRODUCTION OF SCIENTIFIC MANAGEMENT

Is it not necessary, in introducing Scientific Management, to import a number of functional foremen, etc.?

That depends upon circumstances. In our business we have a Flying Squadron of "over foremen" for starting a new job properly. These men are trained to handle one or more functions each, and can therefore start the job under Scientific Management on the first day that they arrive. It is their duty to help the permanently assigned functional foremen to get their work into shape and planned ahead as far as possible. The Flying Squadron can then be spared for other work, yet be available in case of emergency. In starting any new undertaking, for best results a larger number of foremen are required than are needed after the job has progressed.

The Flying Squadron, therefore, is valuable at the start of the work for its actual services as well as for teaching the permanent foremen on the job.

How can you introduce Scientific Management into an organization without giving the business a jolt?

By beginning at those places where the savings will be immediate and where changes will affect the entire establishment least, — by installing it first where it affects the work of one man only at a time, and by progressing at that speed that will not cause a jolt to the business.

TIME NECESSARY TO INSTALL SCIENTIFIC MANAGEMENT

How long will it take to install it all?

It can never be "all" installed, because there is no end to it. The time required differs. For example, the Link-Belt Company spent several years putting Scientific Management into their works at Philadelphia, while they were able afterwards to put the same system into their Western shops in less than the same number of months.

It takes much longer to put it in where the management itself must be taught than where there is a Flying Squadron ready to take up the installation of each function.

In construction work, is not the job nearly completed before Scientific Management can be installed?

As there is no end to Scientific Management, it can never be said to be completely installed. In construction work much benefit can be obtained immediately — greater speed, better quality, and lower costs of production. From the very nature of construction work, it is difficult to avoid waste under any plan of management, and particularly under the traditional plan of management. It, therefore, offers unusual opportunities for saving through Scientific Management installed from the first day by the Flying Squadron.

PRACTICABILITY OF SCIENTIFIC MANAGEMENT

Isn't it true that you cannot expect to get all of the men, in fact any man, to use all of the prescribed motions and only the prescribed motions in any one day, or day after day?

It is quite impossible to get perfection in anything. However, the savings in motions, due, for example, to putting the bricks on a packet the right way in the first place, and delivering the brick to the bricklayer exactly in that condition and position that will make it easiest for him to use the most economical motions, together with the gang boss who is specially trained to coach the bricklayer to use the fewest, most economical, and most efficient standard motions, will result in an extremely high efficiency which, even if it does not reach the 100 per cent mark, is nearer to it daily.

How can an engineer tell with a stop watch, by timing a worker for a few hours or days, how much he can do day after day at his work, and how can the engineer be sure that the worker being timed is not using up his reserve strength?

He cannot be sure without sufficiently painstaking investigation. That is why Dr. Taylor timed men for long periods before he found his laws relating to quantities of rest required for overcoming fatigue without calling upon the worker's reserve strength. No worker has ever considered that he must actually rest two whole hours in a day, yet Dr. Taylor found that some kinds of work required the worker to rest over 50 per cent of his entire day.

Purpose of Scientific Management

Is it not true that under the Taylor System the shop or the business " exists first, last, and all the time for the purpose of paying dividends to its owners "?

Yes, and that is also true about shops and businesses under any and all other forms of management. Without dividends there is no doubt that the best thing to do would be to sell off the machinery before it was all worn out, and to do such other things as might be necessary to get back the capital invested before it was lost.

Expense

Must one " go the whole game " with Scientific Management to get real results?

No. Especially is this true in the small concern where there are not enough employees to warrant the installation of all of the features of Scientific Management. A small concern can use many of the features, however, very advantageously.

Can saving be made, and have savings been made, from the first day?

Savings by use of Scientific Management can undoubtedly be made from the first day. Scientific investigations can undoubtedly be made that will pay for themselves as they go along; but the relation of the saving by Scientific Management to the expense of it varies at different periods, and depends upon how fast Scientific Management is installed and upon the nature of the business.

In our business, we can show hundreds of instances on the cost records of substantial decrease in costs, in many cases of costs that were halved as fast as the system was installed.

Is it not necessary to wait years after Scientific Management is introduced to get full reduction in costs?

Yes, in a business already highly systematized, it undoubtedly will require from 2 to 4 years to get the full benefit of the complete introduction of Scientific Management. This time can usually be reduced when there is no interference from those who oppose through ignorance.

Does not Scientific Management occasion a large outlay for equipment and machinery?

The purpose of Scientific Management is not the installing of the best machinery, although the best machinery is of course desirable. It is using to best advantage the machinery available.

Scientific Management aims, primarily, so to handle labor with the existing machinery that the maximum prosperity will result for the employer and for all employees. But, as it deals largely with scientific investigation, it discovers laws, and points out the economic advantages of new devices and machines. While it makes the employee more efficient and the management of more assistance to the employees, it also predetermines and makes inventions in machinery as well as methods almost obvious. Whether or not additional machinery and equipment is acquired is not a vital part of Scientific Management.

Is not the expense burden of maintaining the planning department equal to all the savings that it can make?

Dr. Taylor answers this in a most concise manner in paragraph 155 in the Transactions of the American Society of Mechanical Engineers, Paper 1003 ("Shop Management," Harper and Brothers, pp. 55–56) : —

"At first view the running of a planning department, together with the other innovations, would appear to involve a large amount of additional work and expense, and the most natural question would be whether the increased efficiency of the shop more than offsets this outlay.

"It must be borne in mind, however, that, with the exception of the study of unit times, there is hardly a single item of work done in the planning department which is not already being done in the shop. Establishing a planning department merely concentrates the planning and much other brain work in a few men especially fitted for their task and trained in their especial lines, instead of having it done, as heretofore, in most cases by high-priced mechanics, well fitted to work at their trades, but poorly trained for work more or less clerical in its nature."

Mr. H. L. Gantt says, page 18, in "Work, Wages, and Profits":—

"A scientific investigation into the details of a condition that has grown up unassisted by science has never yet failed to show that economies and improvements are feasible that benefit both parties to an extent unexpected by either."

Is not Scientific Time Study so expensive that the average job cannot afford it?

Scientific Time Study does not all have to be done on one job. There are certain features that will reduce costs from the first day that can be done on even small jobs. The average job, even the small job, can be helped by many of the features of Scientific Management; and the instruction cards of previous jobs can be used with great economy even on small jobs.

Why are so many more inspectors required if the work is done better under Scientific Management?

Because the instruction cards call for a definite quality. They do not call for having the "work done to the satisfaction" of anybody. The extra money paid to the workers under Scientific Management is contingent upon the prescribed kind of quality being achieved.

The inspector keeps a close watch of work under Scientific Management. It is his duty to detect mistakes or lack of quality before much damage is done. As an example, suppose a workman was ordered to make 100 duplicate pieces from the same drawing. The inspector would watch the first piece keenly during its making and would pass upon the first unit when it was finished, to make sure that the workman understood his duties, and what was expected of him, and also that the quality of the work was right in every particular.

To catch mistakes before they are made is the cheapest way to get the right results.

Furthermore, the inspector under Scientific Management not only inspects, but also assists and instructs the workmen directly instead of through the other functional foremen.

Isn't there a larger waste from spoiling materials under Scientific Management?

There is not, because, as stated elsewhere, the first functional foreman introduced is that of inspector. The work is inspected more systematically under Scientific Management. The bonus is not paid unless the quality is within the requirements of the written instruction card.

The method of inspection under traditional management is often wasteful, because the inspection is usually done after the material is fabricated. Under Scientific Management the inspection proceeds as does the work itself. Inasmuch as the gang boss gets no bonus if the quality is not in accordance with the prescribed quality, he has a constant incentive to play at team work with the workman, *i.e.* he sees that the workman is provided with tools and surroundings in the best condition to make the prescribed quality. It is a matter of history that the quality of output has invariably improved by the introduction of Scientific Management.

INDICATORS OF SUCCESSFUL MANAGEMENT

What indicates the quality of the Management?

The best indicator of the quality of the management is the difference between the *customary* wages given for a certain kind of work and also the usual costs of production for that kind of work in other establishments, compared with the wages given and the costs of production in the works under consideration; or, in other words, the amount that the wages are higher and the amount that the costs of production are lower than usual, indicate the quality of management — other qualities, such as sanitary conditions, being as good or better.

If Scientific Management is all that is claimed for it, why are not the dividends always larger than in any shop where there is no Scientific Management?

They would be, if the merit and quality of the management were the one determining factor in profits and dividends. On the contrary, business judgment as to what and when to buy and where to sell, good salesmanship, and ability to get business at high prices are often of such great importance that dividends can be paid in spite of bad management. On the other hand, there are some cases where the management is so good that dividends can be paid in spite of bad business handling.

CHAPTER IV

EFFECT OF SCIENTIFIC MANAGEMENT ON THE WORKER

ACCIDENTS

Does Scientific Management insure the workman against accidents?

It does not insure him, but it certainly does reduce the number of accidents, because the machines, scaffolds, works, and ways are made and maintained in the standard condition called for on the instruction card, and are regularly inspected and overhauled as directed, and as often as required, by the written orders that come regularly from the Tickler or Reminder File.

Does not intensive production cause rapid depreciation of machinery, causing bad work and accidents and injury to the men?

No, because the desired maintainable standard condition of the machinery is determined by the planning department, just the same as the speed at which it is to be operated. It is inspected, cleaned and oiled, and repaired at stated times, whether it needs it or not. It must be kept up to the standard condition, or the worker cannot get the big outputs called for in order to get his bonus.

Therefore, the machinery is maintained constantly in such a condition that it will not break down or cause

accidents. In fact, this function of repairs and main-
tenance at prescribed condition is assigned to a functional foreman specially trained to look after this work
in accordance with the written instructions furnished
by the planning department.

Does not a bonus scheme cause the work to be slighted and result in accidents to those who work under such conditions?

Yes, it does, when the bonus scheme is applied under
the old plans of management. One man has stated that
"any bonus scheme for repairing locomotives should be
prohibited by laws; because when so many lives are
dependent upon the quality of repairs on a locomotive,
there should never be an incentive to hurry the mechanic
doing the repairs."

Under all of the old forms of "bonus schemes" this is
absolutely true. Dr. Taylor must have recognized this
and all other perfectly obvious difficulties of management in his practice. Dr. Taylor also successfully provided for overcoming this difficulty in a most logical
and efficient manner, as follows: —

First, he analyzed the problem.
Second, he broke it up into its several most elementary
subdivisions.
Third, he applied science to solving the problem of handling each subdivision in the best way.
Fourth, he built up, by and with the advice and assistance
of the best workmen and engineers obtainable, a
complete new process synthetically.
Fifth, he caused to be put in writing the entire process, so
that it could be used forevermore, with all the ad-

vantages that come from conserving the information of how to do a thing in the best known way.

Sixth, he created the function of inspector, with duties of constructive criticism and not destructive criticism. He made it the duty of the inspector to sign a separate paper, stating that each and every repair had been executed precisely in accordance with the demanded quality of workmanship — no better and no worse. He authorized the inspector to deal directly with the workman and to assist him to achieve the prescribed quality of workmanship.

Seventh, he required the foreman to sign a separate piece of paper stating the length of time required to complete the job in the prescribed manner according to the requirements of the instruction card, as certified to in writing by the inspector.

Eighth, he provided that if the workman did the job exactly as prescribed, and certified to by the inspector, and if he also did the job within a certain time, he got a bonus — otherwise he did not.

It is now obvious that on such important matters as repairs on locomotives the Taylor plan is the most efficient for prevention of accidents. In our own experience, we have found that Dr. Taylor's plan is of great assistance in preventing accidents; in fact, we know that it is the one simplest and most efficient method of protecting the workers from injury and loss of life.

Dr. Taylor's plan is usually discussed from the standpoint of reducing costs, raising wages, increasing speed of construction, etc.; but if it had no other merit than its great benefits in eliminating the horrors and wastes due to the injury and killing of human beings, both of the public and of the workers themselves, it would have warranted the life work of Dr. Taylor and his followers spent in the creation of the science.

BRAIN

How can you expect every laborer to understand Scientific Management when it takes an engineer so many years to learn it?

The laborer does not understand it, nor is he expected to understand it. He simply understands the assistance he receives from the functional foremen in learning how to do his work more efficiently. He recognizes that he gets fairer treatment from the disciplinarian, higher wages from the time and cost clerk, and much more help from all the functional foremen; but he does not always learn the theories of Scientific Management unless he is ambitious enough specially to study it and to follow the same road that is open to every one else.

A machinist who has worked under Scientific Management for about one half of the ten years of his experience was asked how he liked the system. His reply was that he didn't know much about the system, because he "personally did not come in contact with it." He further stated that about all he knew of it was that somehow it enabled him to earn about a third more money every week of his life and that he had never been treated as well in any other establishment.

How long will it take any man to learn it?

There will never be a time when the expert will not learn more about it. The more one studies Scientific Management the more one is able to see what there is to learn, and the more experience he has in it the faster he is able to acquire new facts about it.

At the present time it is considered that a liberal education, preferably in engineering, followed by the complete mastery of at least one and preferably several mechanical trades, followed by four to six years of the closest study of the practical applications of the laws of Scientific Management in several widely different kinds of work, should make one capable of installing nearly all portions of Scientific Management into any business. In other words, with the same quality of brains, application, study, and experience, about the same length of time is required as to become a skilled surgeon. The surgeon, however, has the advantage of having at his disposal a tremendous amount of literature on his subject and also educational institutions. These, though quite as desirable, are not in existence in the subject of management. It is to be hoped, however, that this condition will be altered in the future and the time necessary for preparation will be greatly reduced.

Does it not make machines out of men?

Now, this question is usually asked in just this form, but there seems to be a great difference of opinion as to exactly what the questioner means. Is a good boxer, or fencer, or golf player a machine? Is the highly trained soldier at bayonet or saber drill a machine? He certainly approaches closely the 100 per cent mark of perfection from the standpoint of the experts in motion study. It is not nearly so important to decide whether or not he is a machine as to decide whether or not it is desirable to have a man trained as near perfection as possible in accordance with that method that expert investigators, working in harmony with the best actual workers, have decided to be the best known method for executing a given piece of work.

"All-around experience" to-day often means undue familiarity with many wrong methods, and "judgment" too often means the sad memory of the details of having done the work in several inefficient ways with a memory good enough to prevent repeating the use of the worst methods.

It is the aim of Scientific Management to induce men to act as nearly like machines as possible, so far as doing the work in the one best way that has been discovered is concerned. After the worker has learned that best way, he will have a starting point from which to measure any new method that his ingenuity can suggest. But until he has studied and mastered the standard method, he is requested not to start a debating society on that subject. Experience has shown that, with the best men chosen for the special work of selecting the method and planning the various steps in the processes, — these men having facilities and data at their command that equip them for their jobs, — their way will, in most cases, be better than that of the worker who has not first qualified on their way.

Experience has also shown that, whether or not the men may be called machines, they fare better and profit more when the management takes the time to have a trained planning department, coöperating with the best workmen, determining every step in the process, and every motion in the step, and the effect of every variable in the motion. Then, after the "machine" has done it that way, — in the time allowed for the way, — the "machine" will be paid unusually high wages in real money for any suggestions that will be more efficient. He will be promoted to teach the others his new accepted method. If he continues to make suggestions for better methods than those of the planning department, he will be promoted to it. The line of promotion continues still higher; in fact, this "machine" will find himself at the top, if the measuring methods and devices show him to be more efficient than his fellows, for Scientific Management boosts "machines" for efficiency, not for their bluffs, bulldozing, or snap judgment.

Doesn't Scientific Management keep the worker from being an all-around mechanic and instead make him a narrowly trained specialist?

Perhaps so. Is it not better so? When there is so much to learn about such a simple thing as transporting a brick from the street to its final resting place, it is not better for the worker to have 100 per cent of knowledge on one specialty than to have one half per cent of his total knowledge on each of 200 different ways of earning a living. In all the great professions, specialization is the order of the day.

The physician and surgeon is no longer also the dentist. The dentist no longer attempts to do everything in his profession, except in remote places. He specializes in one of the many subdivisions of dentistry. His mechanical laboratory work certainly requires a differently trained expert than does the specialty of orthodontia or prophylaxis

There is so much to learn in any kind of work that the most highly specialized worker can never expect to learn it all.   In the professions, specialization generally means increased standing, usefulness, and earning power.   Experience has proved that this is also true in the arts and trades.

Dr. Taylor has spent years investigating the comparatively simple art of shoveling, and he has said that even yet he has not learned it all.   In case any one feels cramped by narrow overspecialization, he has as further compensation the fact that, if he has learned it all, his brain will be in such rested condition at the close of the working day that he can attend some night manual training school, where motion study, time study, and standardization are *not* taught, and where the faculty prove nightly that the Taylor plan of management, as a practical proposition, is not worthy of his consideration, because if it were they would, of course, teach it.

Perhaps specialization does narrow the mechanic, from the viewpoint of some people, but it does make him a highly trained expert in his specialty.

In case he loses his job under Scientific Management, is he not too highly specialized and not enough of an all-around mechanic to hold a job anywhere else?

The answer is "No." For he has been taught a method of attack that will enable him to use to advantage all the brains he has.   He will have been taught all economies from motion study.   That, in itself, will enable him to excel quickly those workers who have not been so taught. He will have been taught the economies resulting from the use of the instruction card.

If he has been taught to a point where he has been "overspecialized," then he surely has been taught habits of work that will enable him to become quickly a profitable worker at any new work that he may undertake.

Does not the monotony of the highly specialized subdivision of work cause the men to become insane?

No. Until one has worked under Scientific Management, and consequently realizes what the subdivisions mean, one cannot realize the great amount of knowledge that it is possible to acquire on any one subdivision of any one trade. For example, it was not until after we devoted years to the study of the motions used by several mechanical trades that we discovered that with the aid of a few devices we could teach an apprentice to lay brick faster and make a better looking and stronger wall than could an experienced journeyman working in the old manner.

Further study shows that our more recent investigations cause the old methods of bricklaying to be obsolete, for we now can build brick walls by machinery, at a lower cost, with no question as to filling of the joints, stronger, quicker, and drier, and by the same methods can build any kind of arches, ornamental work, etc., as cheaply as straight and plain brickwork can be built under the old method. We now see possibilities of improvement under this new method that seem to have no end. Yet, generally speaking, is not the subdivision of the mason's trade, brickwork, considered as monotonous as any kind of work?

A few years ago it was a general custom all over America, and is still in remote places, for a "mason" to be a stone mason, stone cutter, bricklayer, plasterer, and cement worker. Modern conditions have reclassified these trades, so that even the subclasses of the bricklayers now are divided into several distinct classes. The best plasterers and stone masons can no longer compete with the best bricklayer on brickwork. The plasterer's trade is also subdivided, although not as much as it will be.

To the man who has no leaning toward brain work, there is an ideal place provided in the performing department. When he feels that his work there is monotonous, there are three opportunities open to him —

(a) He may join the planning department.

(b) He may become teacher of the other men who prefer the so-called monotonous work, relieved of all responsibility except to do their work as called for.

(c) He can plan the spending of the extra money that will be in his pay envelope on next pay day, and can consider the intellectual stimulus that the extra pay will purchase; for when work is so highly repetitive as to be monotonous, it will surely enable the man best fitted for that work to earn the highest wages that he can ever earn at any vocation, *because* he has had practice at that work so long that it has become monotonous.

No, he will not become insane, for if his brain is of such an order that his work does not stimulate it to its highest degree, then he will be promoted, for under Scientific Management each man is specially trained to occupy that place that is the highest that he is capable, mentally and physically, of filling, after having had long training by the best teachers procurable.

Does it not rest a man to use different motions and doesn't it refresh his brain to do the work in a different way each time?

As a general proposition, it does *not* refresh a worker to use different motions. When it does, the planning should and does take that into consideration when making out the instruction card. One of the most generally recognized instances of this is the bookkeeper's standing desk and high chair. He changes from sitting to standing and *vice versa*, to rest and refresh himself; yet the motions of work are identical whether standing or sitting. That doing work the same way requires less effort than doing it it a new way is so well recognized that a condition finally results where it seems as if the fingers could do the work with no other assistance than the command from the brain to proceed. This condition is called being "fingerwise" at a piece of work. It is well illustrated by the simple process of "buttoning a button," an act most complicated to the beginner.

Different motions each time require additional effort, a new mental process and a complete decision with the accompanying extra fatigue. The same motions each time take advantage of automaticity of motions, which is often less fatiguing than less wasteful, though constantly differing, motions.

Does not the old-fashioned way of gaining experience or judgment give the worker a training that he would never get otherwise?

Yes. The methods of Scientific Management will deprive him of much of the unnecessary and unproductive part of his experience, in that it will teach him, in the quickest way, how to learn the most efficient method. If he gets such proper training first, it will provide him during his after life with a mental and manual equipment that will serve him in making quick decisions in selecting his future experience, and in judging the "old type of experience" wherever he encounters it later.

"Experience is the best teacher" is as meaningless a proverb as "You can't teach an old dog new tricks." When the best experience has been found, measured, and recognized, it should be made standard, — written down on an instruction card. In this form it can be depended upon to be the best teacher, for it will transmit the information and experience from one mechanic to another without any loss in transmission.

Chance for a Square Deal

How can any one think it fair to take stop watch records on the very best man obtainable and then expect the others of the rank and file to keep up with such records?

Scientific Management does not expect the inefficient man to keep up with the first-class man, neither does it expect a dollar watch to do the work of the $300 watch. But when standards are created they must be founded on the work of the best man procurable, *i.e.* they must be a "100 per cent standard man's" records. Then all due allowance must be made for the difference in quality between the record of the standard worker and the worker who is actually going to do the work.

The poorer quality of men are not able to equal the records of the best men, but the analysis of data will show at what speed each man should work for the best combined results of output and health. Obviously it would add too much to fixed charges to take time study on each man. The present method is, by comparison, cheaper and more just, fair, effective, and satisfactory.

What show of a square deal has a worker who has from "one to eight foremen standing over him at the same time, applying a sort of industrial Third Degree" to make him conform to the desired standard motions?

This question has nothing to do with Taylor's plan of management, for the reason that each foreman helps the worker to do his work in the prescribed manner; teaches him the standard method, and how to use the least fatiguing and non-wasteful motions. Regardless of the number that may be helping him at once, the gang bosses have nothing to do with any "third degree" nor with any other form of discipline. That is all taken care of by an unprejudiced specialist called the "disciplinarian," whose make-up is that of peacemaker and whose duty is the furthering of the square deal.

Chance for Work

When Scientific Management is in full operation, can the management dispense with the good men?

On the contrary, under Scientific Management even the functional foremen are expected to acquire so much more knowledge about their one function than is customary under the traditional plan of management that it will always require particularly good men to fill their positions.

The men, in their turn, that will be required, on account of the large outputs and the close following of the instruction cards demanded, will have to be exceptionally good men of their class. Every man will be expected to be the best obtainable of his respective class. In fact, Scientific Management goes farthest into the subject of selecting men specially fitted for their work. It does, however, demand that a man shall have a great deal of knowledge about his specialty and life work, rather than a little knowledge about many kinds of work.

Not only does Scientific Management require good men after it is in full operation, but it also provides for definite promotion to retain a man after he has outgrown his job. As Mr. James F. Butterworth, a well-known English authority, summed it up in the *London Standard* — "Scientific Management not only quickly recognizes the first-class man, but attracts other first-class men to share in the bettered conditions."

Granted that Scientific Management is advantageous for the best worker, is it not a distinct hardship to the mediocre man?

It is not, because first of all, the best men are promoted out of competition with the mediocre man. Furthermore, every man, including the mediocre man, is taught and promoted to fill the highest place that he is by nature and special training able to occupy. In fact, every man is taught and coached and helped until he reaches an earning power that he never could expect under the traditional form of management. The average man, having been taught a systematic method of attack, is better prepared to handle any new work at which he is put than he ever could if he had not had the experience under the systematic working of Scientific Management.

Does not Scientific Management eliminate many men, *i.e.* actually reduce the number of men employed, according to Mr. Taylor's own words?

No, because the management is enabled to handle more men and thus get the work completed quicker. Furthermore, while it is true that on any one part of the work the men required might be fewer, it is also true that the method of selection itself often results in providing the men, who are eliminated because of natural unfitness, with work for which they in turn are much better fitted. Actual statistics show that there has never been a case where the total number of employees has remained less in any organization operating under Scientific Management.

What would happen if every concern suddenly were able to do its work with one third of its present number of men?

It will take two or three years to install the principal features of Scientific Management in any one concern. It would take a lifetime to install all of the refinements of Scientific Management now recognized and determined. There never has been a case yet where the business being systematized did not employ a total of more men the more highly it was systematized. As soon as the work in any one department can be done with fewer men, the business as a whole becomes so successful that it can underbid its competitors; in fact, it often creates a market for its goods and then requires more men in other departments.

What becomes of the men to-day under the traditional plan of management?

Under this old plan, often the efficient instead of the inefficient man is "weeded out." He is never sure of his job, because usually under the old plan there is no accurate measuring of his efficiency. Where there is, he very often has made a low record of output because of a fault of the management.

Perhaps in some "dependent sequence," his work has been held up by failure of the management to supply him something; for example, the carpenter cannot lay the floor if he is not supplied with nails. The shoveler's output might be low because he had not been furnished with shovels that would permit of $21\frac{1}{2}$ pounds of material on the shovel regardless of the change in the kind of materials shoveled.

"By those who have grasped this fact it is universally held that increased production due to efficiency of labor accrues very largely to the laborers themselves." ("Economics," by Arthur Twining Hadley.)

What happens to unskilled labor under Scientific Management?

Under Scientific Management there is no unskilled labor; or, at least, labor does not remain unskilled. Unskilled labor is taught the best method obtainable, and is provided with a corps of teachers whose duty it is to assist the laborers to become highly skilled in that art or trade at which they work.

Furthermore, the men are promoted as fast as they are fitted to be promoted, and are specially taught to fill places commanding higher wages even while they are taught. No labor is unskilled after it is taught.

Will not Scientific Management result in putting unskilled laborers at mechanics' work?

Not while they are unskilled. It is a part of the system to train all men to perform the highest class of work which they are mentally and physically able to perform. It in no way, however, contemplates the superseding of mechanics; which, of course, would be bad for the mechanics. The mechanics need have no fear from that source; in fact, Scientific Management plans for and entails so high a degree of perfection that the one greatest difficulty it encounters is to secure mechanics of sufficient intelligence, training, and expertness to carry out its plan. It does not concur, however, with the once general belief and principle that a locomotive driver should also be an expert machinist who could build as well as run a locomotive.

Is it not specially hard on the " weaker brothers "?

Yes, if "weaker brothers" means unwilling incompetents. These, Scientific Management discards, as does every other form of management, as fast as they can be detected. Any body of workers who, by purposely hiding the "weaker brother" in the gang, thereby make it difficult and sometimes impossible for the old-fashioned management to detect the weaker brother, is paying for his support out of the pockets of the strong. If this is so, why not measure his ability, pay him accurately what he is worth, pay the strong ones accordingly, and let the strong pay him what extra amount they desire to contribute on account of his weakness? Meanwhile, perhaps, he could be taught, or put on work where he would be more efficient.

Oftentimes a worker is inefficient because he is naturally unfitted for his chosen work by reason of natural slowness of successive action or poor ability for retention in memory of spoken words. Those workers with high personal coefficient, where the inward end organ most used in the work is the eye, as in the work of proofreading, are often the fastest workers when changed to such work, for example, as short-hand, where the impressions on the brain are taken in at the ear.

Again, the measuring devices of Scientific Management often discover that the "weaker brother," or the inefficient sister, is really a square peg in a round hole. While all kinds of management endeavor to discard the inferior workers, Scientific Management is the one plan that makes definite and systematic effort to promote each worker to the highest notch he is capable of in his chosen life work. It tries to place each worker where scientific investigation and analysis of his individual peculiarities indicate that he will be most efficient.

Volumes could be written about the worker who is in the wrong life work, for which he is by nature totally unfitted. The recognition of this fact is the cause for the interest in vocational guidance throughout the country.

We believe that one great benefit derived from Scientific

Management will be the utilization of its data for assisting young men and women in determining the life work for which their particular faculties will enable them to be most efficient. Scientific Management endeavors to discover for workers, before they go to work, that work to which they are best adapted. In fact, the selection of the worker is an act of great importance under Scientific Management, and is one on which great stress is laid.

Scientific Management also tries to discard no man who has been tried out and partially taught. It attempts to place him to better advantage to himself and also to the management.

What happens to the inefficient worker? Is he not thrown out upon the labor market?

There are several things that may happen to him.

(a) He may be taught so that he becomes extremely efficient.

(b) His efficiency will be increased, whatever it is.

(c) He may be placed at a kind of work for which he is better fitted.

(d) He may be placed on that portion of the work that has not been systematized. There has never been a case where the Taylor System caused a large number of unemployed.

Doesn't the Taylor System really plan to eliminate the hopelessly inefficient man?

Yes, and so does every other plan of management. The other plans are not fair in that they do not always determine which are the really inefficient, but leave it to an overworked, busy, uninformed, prejudiced foreman or employer; while under the Taylor System the man is taught, shifted, and taught again, until he is placed at that work at which he is most efficient, and tried and tried until he has demonstrated his entire unfitness.   Meantime, while he may not have been able to earn the maximum wages, he will have earned much higher wages than he could earn anywhere else on similar work under the old form of management.

HEALTH

What regard has this System for the physical welfare of the men?   Does not this System call upon the reserve force of the worker, and thus wear him out before his time?

This question is answered at length by Mr. C. A. E. Winslow, Associate Professor of Biology, College of the City of New York, and Curator of Public Health, American Museum of Natural History, New York, in an intensely interesting paper read before the Congress of Technology on the fiftieth anniversary of the granting of the charter of the Massachusetts Institute of Technology.   Professor Winslow states in the closing paragraph: —

"The cleanliness of the factory, the purity of the drinking water, the quality of lighting, the sanitary provisions, and a dozen other points will suggest themselves to the skilled investigator when on the ground.   He may find in many of these directions economic methods by which efficiency may be promoted."

Have observations ever been made on any one man long enough to determine if Scientific Management benefits him?

Yes, and on hundreds of men.   A visit to the Tabor Manufacturing Co., the Link-Belt Co., and the J. M.

Dodge Co. will convince any one who looks the employees over. There one finds that the men are happier, healthier, better paid, and in better condition every way than the men found in similar work in that vicinity. These places above named are among the shops where Scientific Management in its highest form has been in operation the longest time.

Does not the " speed boss " speed up the men to a point that is injurious to their health?

"Speed boss," like "task," is an unfortunate name, but, as Mr. James M. Dodge has said, the word "task" will probably have to be used until a word that is more descriptive can be substituted for it.

The same thing is true of "speed boss." We have heard one orator state that "the speed boss is the man who drives the slaves." He is right if you call the *machines* the slaves, for the "speed boss" does not tell the men how fast they shall make their motions. He does, however, tell the men at what speeds their machines shall run. He does not drive the men at all. He is their servant. When they cannot make the machines work at the speed called for on the instruction card, it is up to him to do it, then to teach them, or else to report to the planning department that he cannot, and then its members must show and help him. Under the traditional plan of management, swearing at a man is supposed to make him work faster, for the time being at least. The speed boss's job is to swear at the machine if he wants to, but he must attain the speed called for, no faster and no slower, or he does not earn his bonus.

Under the old form of management it sometimes happens that the foreman gets so angry at the machine that he discharges the operator, but the speed boss can not do this under Scientific Management. All cases of discharge must be handled by a trained, quiet disciplinarian, who disciplines the operator, the speed boss, and any one else who needs it, even the superintendent himself. This, in itself, is so unusual that in many cases the average workman cannot understand how it is that he is being treated so fairly.

As a general practice, do the people want a standard of efficiency so high that it requires a stop watch to get "the last drop of blood"?

There is no "last drop of blood" about it! The stop watch is a measuring device that has no more to do with making men work than it has when used by a physician to determine at what rate the pulse is beating. The stop watch is used to determine the correct time necessary for doing a certain piece of work, and to determine how much the worker should rest in order to achieve and maintain his best physical and mental condition.

It must be admitted, even by those who do not understand Scientific Management, that there is some rate of speed which is the correct speed at which the individual worker should work, and that this speed varies according to the man — his birth, education, training, health, and condition.

This correct speed is not the speed at which he would like to work if he were just naturally lazy, but it is the best speed at which he can work day after day, month after month, and, if he has reached the zenith of his promotion, then also year after year, and thrive, and continually improve in health.

The stop watch must be used to insure that the instruction card, the output, the percentage of rest for overcoming fatigue, and the pay shall be based upon that exact speed.

Taylor has found, by use of the stop watch and by timing thousands of cases, that some work requires that a man shall actually rest over 50 per cent of the entire day, and that practically all work requires more than $12\frac{1}{2}$ per cent rest. Now, that is one hour in an eight-hour day, and it does not sound nearly as much like "taking the last drop of blood" as does the old method of management, under which, if the manager heard that the man rested one half hour every day, he saw to it that the man was discharged.

Wherein does it cost the employer anything to lose a worker by wearing him out?

It takes time and costs money to specially train him, and old workers are therefore usually the most desirable.

INITIATIVE

What has Scientific Management to take the place of the ingenious man?

It has nothing "to take the place of the ingenious man." It does not supplant him. On the contrary, it furnishes a specially equipped planning department to help him to further and conserve systematically his ingenuity.

This department works out problems of improvement of methods and conditions.

Such a department puts the services of the ingenious man and the inventor on a business basis and provides measuring devices and methods for determining the numerical measure of the efficiency of the new methods as compared with the old.

Does not the management lose the initiative and the bright ideas of its ingenious employees when they are obliged to follow implicitly the detailed written orders of the instruction card?

No. On the contrary, there is a special department for the employment of those men whose make-up and training specially fit them to make the most numerous and most valuable suggestions for improvements.

The value of the ingenious suggestions of the workmen is specially recognized and provided for by Scientific Management. Not only is a department created and maintained for fostering, conserving, and specially inventing such forms of improvement, but also a cash prize system is in operation for further obtaining the suggestions of those workmen who are outside the regular planning department.

It is seldom appreciated by the layman that the only inventions and improvements that are not wanted are those that are offered by the employee *before* he has first qualified on the standard method of procedure in accordance with the much tried out instruction card.

The condition precedent to an audience for offering a suggestion for an improvement is to have proved that the suggestor knows the standard method, and can do the work in the standard way of standard quality in the standard time. Having thus qualified, he is in a position to know whether or not his new suggestion is a real improvement.

Scientific Management offers the first standard method of obtaining high efficiency from those best qualified to invent and to make new methods. The ingenious employee is specially protected, assisted, and encouraged.

Does not standardization dwarf, wither, and preclude innovation and improvement?

On the contrary, standardization offers a base line from which we can measure efficiency. Inasmuch as the value of the entire scheme of scientific management hangs on time study, much time study must, therefore, be taken and used. This consumes time and costs much money. The fewer the standards the less quantity of time study need be taken.

Therefore, for the best net results, a few well-chosen, first-class standards are much to be preferred to many ill-chosen imperfect standards.

Standardization enables, and offers a constant incentive to, employees to try for better standards, not only for the joy of achieving, but also for the money reward that comes from making a better standard. The history of Scientific Management shows greater improvement under it than under any other plan.

When a man is paid under the day work plan for his time instead of for the quantity of output of prescribed quality, there is little to cause him to devise new methods or ways to increase his efficiency or productivity.

On the other hand, under Scientific Management he being paid for his productivity, there is every incentive to do all that he can, — to invent new ways, less wasteful ways, and to keep himself in the best physical condition to work.

What is there in it for the workman who makes the suggestion?

There are various rewards for accepted suggestions: sometimes cash; sometimes promotion to teacher or gang boss; sometimes the saving that the suggestion makes for a definite period of time; or a combination of the above accompanied by the recognition of having the accepted new tool or method named after the suggestor.

INSTRUCTION

Do not men dislike to be taught by teachers from outside?

Sometimes they do dislike it at first, but they usually like obtaining additional information about their life work, regardless from what source it comes.

Furthermore, the teaching usually comes mostly from the men who have been selected from their own number. The extra money that the teachers get is an added incentive to them to learn, earn more while learning, and thus be better fitted for promotion to the position of teacher.

Don't the workers think they " know it all " to start with?

Many mechanics believe that the best workmen of their trade do know nearly all that is worth knowing about their trade, but the unit cost columns and other devices for measuring efficiency soon shows them that "the way we have always done it" can usually be improved upon.

Do the men really benefit much by the teaching, or does not the benefit all go to the employer?

In re teaching, Mr. William Dana Orcutt says: —

"The ambitious workman of the past has sought to advance himself by attending night school, and in other ways which are a strain upon the time which he requires for rest and recreation. Scientific Management gives him this opportunity, under the most skillful instructors, while actually employed in his day's labors, fitting him, at the expense of the concern which employs him, to become qualified to earn higher wages from the very source which gives him his education."

What incentive has the teacher to see that the workers are properly trained?

The teacher's promotion depends on his success in getting results from the workers under his instruction.

He also gets a bonus every time that a worker gets a bonus and a second or double bonus every time that every worker in his entire gang gets a bonus.

Does not Scientific Management do away with the old " journeyman " idea, and is not that of itself a distinct disadvantage to the men?

It does sometimes do away with the "old journeyman idea" in many ways, especially with several of its wasteful aspects. It does away with teaching the apprentice by word of mouth by the traditionally taught journeyman, who has no idea of pedagogy. It does away with taking advantage of an apprentice for a certain definite number of years, just because he is an apprentice. It pays the apprentice in accordance with the quality and quantity of his output, instead of paying him a boy's wages even when he does a man's quantity of work.

It does away with the infamous and common practice of limiting the age at which an apprentice may start to learn his trade. It recognizes no such rule as that a boy shall not begin to lay brick after he is eighteen and shall not be out of his time before he is twenty-one, regardless of how expert he may be. It accords no special favors to any boy because his father was of the trade at which the boy works.

It substitutes for all this a square deal and a more efficient method of teaching the trade to a boy. It enables him to learn faster, to learn the science of his trade, to learn the best method that science can devise. It furnishes specially taught teachers to give "post-journeyman instruction" to even its best men. It makes available for use as a wage-earning device all of the expert knowledge that constant investigation, analysis, and study can devise, collect, and conserve.

Does not the paying of the bonus to the foreman make him help the best workers and let the poorer workers shift for themselves?

He must also help the poor workers or he does not get his second bonus, as the task set is achievable by any persistent worker. As the records of the foremen's gangs are watched by the superintendent, any foreman who does not teach all of his men so that they all can attain their task would not last long at his job.

LEISURE OR REST

Granted that workers "soldier," what is the harm? Does not that rest them?

A certain percentage of rest is necessary for the workers. It is absolutely required for their health. Under Scientific Management the amount of rest is determined scientifically; it is not guessed. The men are required to rest. On our own work we have demonstrated that regular enforced rest periods have invariably resulted in reduced costs of production. Soldiering is a case of making believe that outputs are produced when they are not. It is the worst form of cheating that there is. It often makes men work as hard in pretending to work as they would in actually producing output. Soldiering results in lower wages to the workers and in a business decline to the community.

LIFE, LIBERTY, AND THE PURSUIT OF HAPPINESS

Does not Scientific Management interfere with the workman's personal liberty?

If by that is meant the privilege of doing the work any way he chooses, or by any method, or on a standard of quality other than that prescribed, the answer is certainly "yes." But in every other respect, "no." His freedom from petty graft and holdup, and the protection and square deal offered him, give him more net liberty than he receives under any other plan of management.

Does not the forcing of the workmen to use the specified motions of the System only, from the time they arrive in the morning until they leave at night, take away their liberty and enforce slavery conditions upon the workers?

It has never been contemplated to prescribe each and every motion from the time of arrival to the time of departure in a mill or on a job any more than on a golf course or a baseball field. It is, however, hoped and expected that those motions that are of no use will be eliminated as far as possible, and that the motions used will be limited as far as possible to those that produce output or cause restful exercise. Surely no thinking man wants the work so arranged that the worker makes useless motions, — useless either to himself or to his employer.

Go to any library or sporting goods store, and you can obtain many books with copious illustrations reproduced from photographs to illustrate how to make the exact motions for the greatest efficiency in many different kinds of sports. But in how many trades can similar books be found? The best example to date of applying the motion studies of the arts of war to the arts of peace can be seen in Dr. Taylor's book "On the Art of Cutting Metals." In this he shows photographs of the stages in forging and sharpening metal cutting tools.[1]

Is it slavery to insist that a column of the same figures shall always be added up to the same total?

It seems reasonable, for the greatest efficiency and earning power, that each workman should be taught the

[1] See also "Bricklaying System," M. C. Clark & Co., Chicago, and "Motion Study," D. Van Nostrand, New York.

exact prescribed motions that have been found to be the most productive, the least fatiguing, and the least wasteful. There is more to the benefits of teaching the exact motions than is commonly appreciated by the layman.

The advantage in speed, productivity, and ease of performance that come from habits of exactly the same sequence of motions and the absence of the mental process of making a complete decision for each motion cannot be appreciated by any one who has not made this subject a life study. The saving from this feature is a large one. For the best results, the best sequence of the best motions should be taught first, — taught and insisted upon until that sequence of those motions has become a fixed habit. Necessary and advisable deviations from this sequence will take care of themselves thereafter.

A book could be written on the *advantages of teaching the right motions before insisting upon perfection in the product manufactured.* In other words, Scientific Management insists that the novice shall use certain motions in a certain sequence until he can execute the work in the standard way, for the gains made by this process more than pay later for any cost of the time of the skilled worker going over and fixing up the first work of the unskilled worker. The ancient belief that a worker should do his work of *right quality of output first,* and fast afterward is wholly wrong. He should do his work with the *right motions first,* and either he or some one else should afterwards correct his work, or else throw it away, until he has formed habits of the correct motions. This method not only teaches him much quicker, but it also makes him much more efficient his whole lifetime.

I have never known a mechanic who had been taught the right motions who did not pity those who had not. Those who have only an academic knowledge of perspiration as a means of earning a livelihood should be comforted by the knowledge that the "slave of motion supervision" will have a pay envelope of much greater purchasing power to compensate him for his "slavery."

Does not Scientific Management "trammel the workman in the durable satisfactions of life"?

Not unless it is dissatisfying or unsatisfying to receive the best instruction obtainable and to do work in that method which time and experience have shown to be the least wasteful, the most productive, and the least fatiguing.

Furthermore, the working hours represent but about one half of the total time that the worker is awake. Under Scientific Management he has to work more regularly, and more constantly, but usually at not much greater speed. If this goes against his grain, it is more than compensated for by the greater amount of "durable satisfactions of life," as Dr. Eliot phrases it, that can be purchased with the excess money in the pay envelope earned under Scientific Management.

Why insist that men work separately instead of in gangs when, if they are in gangs, the best men will cause the slow and lazy men to work harder?

Experience proves that the output — when all men have their outputs measured separately — is much greater than when their collective outputs are measured as a gang.

Furthermore, the workers sooner or later argue to themselves in this wise, *i.e.* "What is the use of my working harder than any one else, since the results of my efforts are divided up among the gang?" Furthermore, a man realizes that, even if he rests considerably, it affects the average output of the entire gang very little proportionally, — and, as a matter of fact, the men do not make the lazy ones work. For an example of this see "Philosophy of Management," page 75.

In exactly what way can the men produce more output under Scientific Management?

In *Harper's*, February, 1911, page 433, Mr. William Dana Orcutt, after seeing the results of the installation of the Taylor System by Mr. Morris L. Cooke at the Plimpton Press, says: —

"Every task of the operative is preceded by preparatory coöperation on the part of his employer. When the order reaches him, every detail has been provided for: he has no questions to ask; the proper tools are placed beside him, and the materials themselves are near at hand. All his time is spent upon productive labor, and his output is proportionally increased."

PROMOTION

What show for promotion or development has a young man in a plant operated under Scientific Management?

Every show that there is, except pull. Pull might get the job for him; but he must have the merit, or the record of production and the unit cost records will show him up at his true value.

H. L. Gantt says, page 135 in "Work, Wages, and Profits":—

"The development of skilled workmen by this method is sure and rapid, and wherever the method has been properly established, the problem of securing satisfactory help has been solved.

"During the past few years, while there has been so much talk about the 'growing inefficiency of labor,' I have repeatedly proved the value of this method in increasing its efficiency, and the fact that the system works automatically, when once thoroughly established, puts the possibility of training their own workmen within the reach of all manufacturers."

How can every man be sure that his merit will be discovered and that he will be promoted to the highest notch he can fill?

Because under Scientific Management the output of each man is recorded separately and the relative scores show up constantly.

High scores of output are accompanied by correspondingly high wages.

High scores and wages attract the attention of the management, which needs the services of teachers selected from those men who can make high records of outputs.

From the position of teacher the upward progress for the capable man is rapid.

Admitted that Scientific Management is better for most employees, what have you to offer to the successful all-around foreman under the traditional plan?

The "all-around" foreman, as his very name indicates, has to do many kinds of work, and to perform many different subdivisions of the several functions.

Not only is he in all probability much more efficient in some of his "all-around" duties than in others, but he is also using his valuable time in handling work that could be done by a lower-priced man.

Scientific Management offers such a foreman an opportunity to work constantly at his high-priced specialty. Thus he is more efficient, and we all enjoy that work most that we can do best. His earning power is also increased by putting him on high-class work on which he is most productive, and relieving him of ALL PAY-REDUCING DUTIES that could and should be done by a lower-priced man.

Further, he is taught the best methods that science can discover, — which raises him as a producer and earner above the earning power of his best work at his specialty.

Is it not a system of promotion based upon the contest principle — *i.e.* that the man who has the least regard for his fellows, coupled with the most ability, wins?

The traditional plan of management is sometimes based upon the contest principle; and so in a way is the Taylor plan, but under the Taylor plan, the winner does not win the loss of the loser, as he does under the old plan. On the contrary, the man even with the lowest score is paid unusually high wages, if he achieves his task, regardless of how much more some other worker may do. In other words, all may be winners under Scientific Management. It is not a case of *who* will get the prize by beating the others. It is a case of *how many* will get the prizes. For there are prizes for each and all that can be obtained by paying attention to business constantly.

SPEED

At what speed does Taylor's plan expect any man to work?

At that speed which is the fastest at which he will be happy and at which he can thrive continuously.

Does Scientific Management permit speeding up in case two girls wish to race?

There is nothing in Scientific Management that would prevent two girls from racing if they chose to do so. While Scientific Management does not encourage racing, it could not step in and stop any one from producing as much as he wished without being accused of desiring to limit the amount that could be earned in a day.

The quantity of output prophesied by time study as being the correct amount of output a worker should do in a day can invariably be exceeded by a spurt or a race.

One honest investigator was much disappointed by discovering that Scientific Management did not place a maximum on output of some women workers, — not realizing that such an occasional race to determine which was the smartest between girls who did not have time to enter athletic sports, gave them much pleasure as well as considerable extra money. They had no fear of a subsequent cut in their rate. Their racing record also proved that the set task based upon a high percentage of absolute rest for overcoming fatigue was so far below the record of race output that it was in no way unreasonable for everyday performance.

" Shortened hours combined with increased speed make the conditions of employment more favorable for high-grade labor and less favorable for low-grade labor. The better laborer does not dislike the speed and enjoys the time saved." — Arthur Twining Hadley in " Economics."

Do athletic contests between workers of different nationalities cause race feeling?

We have used the principle of the athletic contest for raising the efficiency of management for a quarter of a century.

Before and since we began the study of Scientific Management we have never seen any reason for criticism of the athletic contest. A periodical recently said that by means of putting different races against one another in atheletic contests, we created race hatred. On the contrary, we have never seen a case of race prejudice result from athletic contests, but we have often seen a keen interest and joy created by such contests. Furthermore, the workmen coming from the same country or district often have the same or similar methods of working, and much can be learned when two or more gangs with different methods are having a friendly contest against each other. The workers are given the pleasure of sport together with a day that passes quicker and brings higher earnings.

Does not the giving of a bonus to the foreman every time that a man earns a bonus result in the foreman driving the men unmercifully so that he can get the bonus offered to tempt his selfish interest?

No, because the task is set by carefully timing actual performance with the proper allowance of time for rest and unexpected delays. No driving is necessary after the workers have been taught the improved method devised by the best workers coöperating with the planning department. After the workers have learned the right improved method they will find it possible to do their task every day by simply working steadily without rushing. When this is not perfectly possible, the task has been set wrong and must be corrected without delay.

Does the practice of paying a bonus to the gang boss for each workman under him, and a double bonus to the gang boss for every day that every man in his gang earns his bonus, result in cruel driving of the worker, and abuse, discharge — in fact everything possible to coerce the worker into earning his bonus even on days when he is sick?

The "gang boss" gets one bonus for each time that the man under him gets a bonus, and a double bonus when every man under him earns his bonus. This makes the interests of the workmen and the gang boss identical. It makes them pull together. It causes the gang boss to do what he can to surround himself with the men who are best fitted by nature to do their allotted work. After these men have been selected, it is for the gang boss to protect and help them in every possible way to earn their unusually high wages, for he cannot get his otherwise. He uses all the brains he owns to help them from morning till night, regardless of how unsympathetic he may be by nature. He will spend no time scheming to get the old employees out and his friends and relatives in, for he realizes that the management has accurate measuring devices of the efficiency of the men under him and of him as an executive. He cannot bluff them. The facts will show up in their true condition in the unit cost column and on the chart showing fluctuations of outputs and individual earnings. The gang boss cannot discharge the workmen, for that is not his function. He will not recommend discharge for slight infractions, personal grudges, etc., because he realizes that to discharge a workman means to train a new one, — with a period when it is probable that at least one workman will not be able to earn his bonus. This means that during all that period the gang boss loses his double bonus plus the single bonus for the one or more men who did not make their bonus. Thus the gang boss thinks more than twice before he disturbs the usual daily working conditions.

Thus it will be seen that the effect of the single and double bonus on the gang boss is, in many ways, to make the employment of the employee more stable and permanent, and an incentive to conserve and use the special ability and efficiency of the trained worker. The gang boss cannot discharge or fine; and it is of no use to abuse the worker, for to recommend punishment that is not approved by the disciplinarian makes the gang boss ridiculous and subject to discipline himself.

Therefore the one thing left is to help the worker, — to help him to do his work, to achieve his task; to see that he gets his tools and materials without delay; and to see that the indication of hindrance or delay by breakdown is reported immediately to the repair boss, whose functions are to make inspections at stated intervals and to keep all machinery in the prescribed condition of repair so that breakdowns do not occur. Under the old scheme the gang boss usually "feels his oats." He abuses or ridicules, and is too busy to help the worker who is discouraged or is falling behind in his record of output.

Under Scientific Management it is better for the gang boss to risk ruin to his suit of clothes by jumping in and helping a man who is delayed by the happening of the unexpected than to let that one incident prevent him from earning the double bonus. Every time he thus helps himself he is helping the worker. There is no parallel to this under the traditional plan of management, except in the very small business where the employer is his own and only gang boss. This condition of scientific management has also many by-products of benefit to the workman. It fosters good feeling between the men and their employers. The men have more contented minds. They dare to push their work, knowing that when they really want help they can always get it. They soon learn to know that the gang boss is working for them, instead of their working for him. Their instructions are in writing on the instruction card. The gang boss can't change those instructions. If they work in accordance with the directions on the instruction card, the disciplinarian will stand by them. If they do not understand their instructions or cannot obey, they send for the gang boss. He is their coach, their tutor, and as the worker is paid more money for being more efficient, so also is the gang boss tutor paid in the form of bonuses and double bonuses in proportion as he is efficient as a teacher — not as a driver. The extra bonus offered to the worker is sufficient to induce him to put forth his best maintainable effort without the additional driving method of the "good old-fashioned" method of management.

UNIONS

Is not the real plan of Scientific Management to disband the unions?

The plan of Scientific Management in no way contemplates the disbanding of the unions. In fact, all followers of Taylor recognize the general necessity for the existence of unions. No one can study the subject of management without appreciating the good that has come as a result of the unions insisting upon more sanitary conditions of the shops and safer conditions of the buildings. It is unfortunate that the unions have not always been right, but they have not. Neither have the employers associations always been right. The many times that each side has been wrong have been due to fear of injury in the future or revenge for real or fancied wrong in the past. But Scientific Management now provides accurate measuring methods and devices for determining the merit and efficiency of different methods of procedure, and the greater the accuracy of such measuring devices, the fewer the misunderstandings between the employer and employees.

The measuring devices find the facts and thus eliminate the largest part of the cause for labor disputes. Mr. George Iles, in his intensely interesting and valuable book, "Inventors at Work," calls attention to the absolute dependence of advance in all sciences on the use of measuring devices. It was the discovery and adaptation of the simple measuring methods and devices by Dr. Taylor that enabled him to make the greatest progress in the science of management and to eliminate war between the employer and labor unions.

These methods of measuring the relative efficiency of methods and men assist to eliminate industrial warfare. Instead of having war, the unions will recognize that under Scientific Management they obtain more money, shorter hours, fairer treatment, better teaching, and more sanitary conditions than their union asks from employers operating under the old-fashioned or traditional plan of management. There must always be unions; there must always be collective bargaining by the unions for some things; but the union that attempts to interfere by collective bargaining with the installation or progress of Scientific Management will, if unsuccessful, have its members left out in the cold, and, if successful in interfering with the management's installation, will so discourage the management that they will decide to postpone, for the time being or permanently, that one plan of management that will enable the workers to obtain unusually high wages. Neither the followers of Taylor, nor any one else, is able to install Scientific Management and simultaneously participate in a debating society or risk results of unfavorable decision of a well-meaning but uninformed board of arbitration.

I cannot emphasize too strongly to any and all labor unions that my advice is to offer no resistance whatever to any employer who is honestly trying to put in Dr. Taylor's plan of management.

After it has been put in and is in fairly smooth running order, the union men will find that their wages are much higher; that the hours are at least no longer — in fact are often shorter; that conditions are better from a health standpoint; and that, further, the square deal really does and must exist. Incompetents holding down positions due to graft, relationship, marriage, and "affinities," are measured up to their true value, and all can see this. The worker's job is sure, so long as he is efficient; the worker is reproved, disciplined, punished, laid off, or discharged by a trained disciplinarian and not by the whim of a suddenly exasperated gang boss, foreman, superintendent, or new manager. When the new manager handles this function of disciplining in any other way than with the square deal, then there is no longer Scientific Management.

This plan of Scientific Management extends and prolongs the years of productivity of the worker, not only because he is treated better, but also because it is entirely a teaching plan; and the old employee can teach for years after his usefulness would have ceased under the old plan of management.

There is no call for unions to cease or disband. If they do disband, it will be because they themselves decide that there is another way of obtaining a better result. The unions have nothing to fear from Scientific Management except that their own acts may unintentionally prevent its rapid installation.

If Scientific Management is a good thing for the workers, why do the labor leaders all oppose it?

They do not all oppose it. Some oppose it for the simple reason that they do not understand it; the others have visions that Scientific Management is something that will reduce the value of their jobs, — and all are afraid, because of the bad treatment that workmen as a whole have had in the past, that Scientific Management is simply a new "confidence game," presented in a more attractive manner than ever before. Because of the many cases of unfair treatment that the workmen have themselves experienced and have seen on every side, they simply cannot imagine Dr. Taylor or any other practical man working for their interests unless there is a " comeback " somewhere.

I have heard gentlemen considered well balanced in every other particular admit privately on one day that they knew nothing of the details of Scientific Management, and harangue a crowd on the following day telling of the evils of Scientific Management to the workingman.

As a matter of fact, there are but few men who, after having first become proficient mechanics in at least one trade, and after having been in direct responsible charge of engineering or mechanical construction, or manufacturing, for several years, can grasp in less than three to five years the fine points of Scientific Management that are necessary to make its operation successful.

Dr. Taylor and his followers, therefore, ask all those who do not understand this plan of management to suspend judgment not only until they understand it, but also until after they have had time and opportunity to talk to those mechanics and laborers who have worked and prospered under it for several years.

In this connection I would recommend for such interviews as typical examples of happy, loyal, intelligent, well-treated, and well-paid workers, employees of the Link-Belt Co., the James M. Dodge Co., and the Tabor Company at Philadelphia.

Is it absolutely necessary to have no collective bargaining in order to install the Taylor System of Management?

No. But it will take longer if such bargaining is introduced. It would be like collective bargaining of the doctors with all the patients in a hospital as to what medicine Patient No. 40 should take.

WAGES

If the worker produces three times more output under Scientific Management than he does under the traditional plan, why does he not get three times as much wages?

If all of the saving by use of Scientific Management were given to the worker, the management could not afford to maintain the corps of investigators and teachers who are necessary under Scientific Management. The saving by means of better processes, easier conditions, and more efficient teaching is so great, however, that increases in wages of 25 to 100 per cent to the workman are always paid. The balance of the saving goes to pay for the cost of maintaining the conditions of Scientific Management and also for reducing costs of production.

In other words, the corps of investigators and teachers is what enables the worker to achieve three or more times the size of the output customary under the "good old-fashioned" management. The savings caused thereby must first pay for this corps, then the balance is divided between the employer and the employees.

What guarantee has the workman that the rate will never be cut?

There may be no guarantee to the workman that the rate will never be cut; but there will be no Scientific Management left if the rates are once cut, because the entire framework of Scientific Management hangs on first having the rate set by Scientific Methods and then never cutting the rate. Scientific Management represents the highest form of coöperation between the employee and the management. No management can expect any coöperation if the workmen have experienced a cutting of the rate with its after effects, namely, systematic soldiering. When the workers are caused by the cutting of a rate to figure out the greatest amount of output they can safely produce without another cut in their rate, there cannot be any further coöperation. Any one who has studied the subject of management enough to install Scientific Management will realize that the rates must be set right the first time and *never* cut. This is the best guarantee the worker can have.

What does the workman get if he exceeds the task?

That depends upon the method of payment that is used. Sometimes a higher piece rate for the entire number of pieces, as under Taylor's differential rate piece system; sometimes the same piece rate for all the additional pieces as the rate per piece of the task. If he exceeds the task much, he will be given a chance at the

job of teacher or of gang boss, at either of which positions
he can earn high wages.

**Does not the management sometimes take advantage
of the disciplinarian's power to fine the workmen and
increase fines in times of business depression?**

No, for the reason that under Scientific Management
the fines collected go back into the pockets of the workman in some form or other.

Bitter strikes have occurred in many of the textile
trades under the old plans of management, because the
fines which were established primarily to compensate
the employers for the injury caused by the employee
were afterwards used as a means of reducing production
costs, by the simple process of fining the workers for everything for which an excuse could be found.

Under Scientific Management the fines collected by the
management for carelessness, disobedience, injury to machines or product are contributed to by the workers, gang
bosses, functional foremen, and even those still higher up,
at any time that the disciplinarian, in the exercise of his
fair judgment, so decides.   The money which is so collected is the nucleus of a sick benefit, insurance or enter-
tainment fund, and is spent wholly upon the workers.

Such an arrangement offers no inducement to the manager or his disciplinarian to be unfair.   The worker does
not so much begrudge the money he has to pay, and every
time the others hear of a fine being imposed they laugh
in their sympathy, because they know the offender must
pay and the management does not profit thereby.   There
is, therefore, no incentive for increasing fines in times of

business depression, or at any other time. Then there is another benefit from the worker's standpoint. It is to the interests of the management to help the workers to do their work with the smallest amount of fines, because the management does not get the income from the fines, and any kind of fines, even necessary fines, cause some hard feeling. It puts the incentive on the management to remove the cause for fines.

What do you do with the bonus if the union refuses to allow the workman to accept it?

When the men refuse to accept high pay that has been offered to them, it should be deposited in a local savings bank subject to their order at any time. If they have earned the bonus that the management has promised them, then the management certainly should not keep it. Depositing it in the local savings bank shows good faith on the part of the management. When the worker gets old and helpless, he may change his mind and draw out his money.

CHAPTER V

What can the colleges and schools do to help Scientific Management; or, what place have the colleges in Scientific Management?

This question is too large to attempt to answer in this book to the extent that it deserves. (See Bulletin #5, Carnegie Foundation, by Mr. Morris L. Cooke, M. A. S. M. E.)

There are five things, however, that would help tremendously: —

1. The colleges should arrange for the collection and interchange of time study data through a central bureau, preferably a national bureau at Washington.

2. They should establish laboratories for the study of methods for shortening the hours of the working day and for increasing the efficiency of the workman, foreman, and manager, that their earning powers may become greater.

3. They should study the reclassification of the trades, that they may be less wasteful and better suited to modern conditions. At the present time nearly all the trades are practiced to suit conditions now obsolete.

4. They should disseminate information and data regarding the economic benefits to the workers them-

selves, as well as the country at large, from having everybody as efficient as possible and constantly producing as large outputs as possible *per unit of time consumed*, so that honest men will not oppose labor-saving machinery because of ignorance of facts.

5. They should disseminate the new method of teaching the trades, realizing: —

(*a*) That the best and fastest workman and the one who can accomplish the greatest output with the least fatigue is he who has been taught the right motions first, speed second, and quality third;

(*b*) That the worker's accuracy at first should be judged by his accuracy in conforming to the standard method and not by the degree of accuracy of his resulting work;

(*c*) That this method is not a scheme for teaching slipshod results but, on the contrary, greater precision. Habits of correct method will result in habits of correct results.

How does Scientific Management affect the general welfare of the country?

Will Irwin says, page 949, *Century*, April, 1910: —

"To get the most out of a day's work and that without injury to the workman's permanent powers, this is the greater formula upon which the pioneers of the new régime are working. Carry the formula to its logical conclusion and it embraces all those movements, formerly in the hands of philanthropists and charitable organizations, which seek to ameliorate working conditions. As a matter of self-interest, it incorporates the golden rule into the theory of production."

What relation has Scientific Management to industrial education?

Scientific Management concurs with the new thought that ideal teaching in the school and college is but the putting of the student in condition to learn his real lessons, namely, those that he will learn out upon the work; and there is no end to these lessons.

Under the old plan the journeyman of each trade is supposed to teach the apprentice his trade. This method is an acknowledged failure, because there is more incentive to the journeyman to keep the apprentice from learning than there is to teach him. This is indirectly recognized by the unions in their laws governing more favored apprentices, such, for example, as the son of a member of the craft whom they know will have the best training that his father, at least, and perhaps his father's most intimate fellow-craftsmen, will give him.

The apprentice is taught so poorly and becomes efficient so slowly that he oftentimes becomes discouraged of ever learning his trade. These two conditions have in the past caused the term of apprenticeship to be five to seven years in England and America, and in the former country that is still the term in many trades. This length of apprenticeship is supposed to give the employer sufficient time to obtain enough profit from the boy's latter years to make up for his former years, when he was unskilled and wasted much material. In fact, the apprentice was so profitless that the master usually made him do other work, such as heavy labor outside his trade, chores about the master's house, errands, etc., in order to get some profit out of the apprentice during the first years of his apprenticeship. The apprentice, obtaining little or no money for wages, in some cases going into debt to pay the employer to teach him his trade — his life work — was usually in constant trouble because he was not being taught as fast as he thought he should be, and was put to other unpleasant work, on the one hand, and was not working as hard as he should, on the other. Under the best of the conditions, he was paid for his time and not for his output — was working on a " day work " basis with an agreed upon wage for a term of years without any definite agreed upon quantity of output that he should deliver in return. His teachers were of two kinds: those that did not care to teach him, and those that were not selected for their ability to teach, even if they were willing. Furthermore, if they happened to be those that were willing and could teach, they taught what *in their opinion* was the best and most efficient method — without any help of modern methods of research and pedagogy. Consider the stupendous waste of this method as compared with the method of teaching the trades under Scientific Management, where the teacher holds his position because of his measured efficiency to teach the one best way that science and coöperation have determined and selected.

It is here that the teachers in the trades schools will soon come into their own. In the past they have suffered from a lack of the proper method of attack that made them become content with graduating boys who, with a little actual "experience" after graduation, could earn journeyman's wages. These were, even then, looked upon as "incubator chickens."   Now, with the method of attack furnished by motion study, time study, and exact methods and devices for measuring the ultimate subdivisions of mental and manual effort and fatigue, the teachers of our trades schools will soon be able to turn out "teachers of mechanics," that is, foremen; and the journeyman who does not learn his trade with the right motions first, and with all other recognized methods for the elimination of unnecessary waste, must take the place of him with the lesser skill.

The faithful old journeyman was a most inefficient worker at best — a less efficient teacher for lack of knowledge and incentive.

The best teacher of the present in the trades schools suffers in salary for lack of appreciation.   The teacher of the future will be the best obtainable.   He will be able to prove his efficiency by the measured quality of his output. This incentive for the teaching of the apprentice by specially trained teachers or functional foremen continues through the entire life of the worker.   There is no end to the period of learning.   Under Scientific Management a worker is better prepared each day to learn the new lessons that the investigators of the planning department have discovered or synthesized.   The functional foremen and teachers of the management are better prepared each day to pass their information on.   The appreciation of the merit of the best teachers of the trades in the future will carry with it an adequate financial compensation.

Is Scientific Management a factor in securing industrial peace?

Mr. William Dana Orcutt says, *Harper's*, February, 1911 : —

"It has commonly been accepted that the interests of capital and labor ought to be identical yet, as a matter of fact, they have rarely been so considered.

"The new force, which is called 'Modern Scientific Management' says, 'If they are not identical, then make them so,' and having flung the banner bearing this slogan to the wind, it has thus separated itself from the systems and systematizing, from card indices, vertical filings, and cost tabulations. It recognizes all these as necessary details of system, which in turn is a necessary ingredient of Scientific Management — but as a science it concerns itself with cause and effect rather than with records or figures, which are usually obtained so late that they possess only historical value."

Is it not a scheme that will wedge apart the college man and the mechanic into opposed classes?

On the contrary, it is the one thing that will show the college-trained man and the young mechanic their interdependent relations. It furnishes an accurate measure of their relative importance. It shows them that for the best and most lasting efficient results they must work together and pull together; that each is absolutely necessary to the other in this plan of Scientific Management, not only during the period of transition from the traditional plan of management, but also after it has been installed and is on a permanent basis.

Does not Scientific Management remove the worker farther than ever from the management?

On the contrary, it brings him into closer touch with the management. He is treated as an individual and is not herded into a gang and treated always as one of a gang. He finds that by coöperating with the management in enforcing its system he raises his own wages, helps his fellow worker to earn more money, and helps the management to get lower production costs. This in turn helps his employer to compete successfully and therefore to secure more business, thus helping to prolong the employment of the workers.

National Industrial Supremacy

Would it not be better to nip the whole Scientific Management movement in the bud because of what will happen to us when the Chinese and Japanese, with their few requirements and low cost of living, discover and apply our methods of attack and laboratory methods as applied to the Science of Management?

Even if there were any force to this argument, it would be lost because it is now too late.

Native Asiatic engineers who have been educated in American colleges have already started the movement of giving their countries the benefits of Scientific Management.

How does Scientific Management affect reclassifying the trades?

First, its records show what parts of the work cause a lowering of the pay of the highly skilled man.

Second, Scientific Management endeavors to have each man so placed that he may work continuously on that kind of highest paying work that his skill, experience, and knowledge will permit him to do.

What place has Scientific Management in vocational guidance?

The preparation of the workman for his life work should begin while he is at school.

See "The Vocational Guidance of Youth," by Meyer Bloomfield, Director of the Vocation Bureau of Boston, lecturer on Vocational Guidance, Harvard University.

What place has so-called welfare work in Scientific Management?

The word "welfare" is usually disagreeable to the ears of the workers. Their viewpoint is that if there is any money to spare for welfare work they would rather have it distributed *pro rata* in their pay envelopes every Saturday night. Any kind of welfare work is better than nothing, and will help some; but to be permanent in its effect such work must be of a kind that enables the worker to be more efficient, to earn more wages, and thus take care of himself without any outside help.

The most beneficial "welfare work" would be the creation of a government bureau for the collection, preservation, and dissemination of data referring to Scientific Management.

Scientific Management hangs upon the science of time study. Dr. Taylor first called attention to the need of a book of time study data on the arts and trades, in 1895. There is not such a book on the market to-day, seventeen years later. Yet the government has employed experts to study how to increase the productivity of sheep, hens, cows, bees, pigs, and Rocky Mountain goats.

Who will be the man to receive the everlasting fame of being the first to start the movement for the permanent creation of a bureau and museum at Washington for the study of Scientific Management and methods of increasing the efficiency, longevity, and productivity of human beings?

Politicans recognize the great value of such a government department, but they are "vote shy." They fear the votes of a great number of workers who honestly believe that the sum total of "working opportunity," as they call it, is fixed and constant, and that to make one man more efficient and thus cause him to be able to do two men's work is simply displacing one more man to be added to the great army of the unemployed. The fact that this may be so this week blinds them to the fact that Scientific Management will quickly bring lasting benefits to them in the immediate future.

The case of the man who made the knitting machine for silk stockings in the time of Queen Elizabeth; the struggles to introduce the sewing machine, and the fountain trowel, and all the wars against the installation of labor-saving machinery since, are too well known to warrant writing about here. These improvements have come and are coming. Nothing can resist them permanently.

It is, however, a national, yes, a world calamity, that there are so many against any plan for saving labor. I am not able to see why, for example, certain unions insist, as did the bricklayers of Glens Falls, that outputs shall be limited by such crude methods as insisting that the bricklayer shall not lay down his trowel when he is picking up brick. They insist that the bricklayer shall not pick up brick with both hands unless he also keeps the trowel in his hand.

I do not understand by what measuring device or method they have determined that that procedure is the exact one that is best for their craft. If small outputs and long hours are desired, why not go the limit and say that no bricklayer shall have a trowel larger than the pie knife used in that vicinity, or that the wristband of the left shirt sleeve of each bricklayer shall be pinned to the leg of his trousers between the hours of eight to twelve and one to five? This surely sounds ridiculous, but four hours of it daily would cut down outputs less than the other less noticeable rules of the Glens Falls bricklayers.

No friend of the working men can do his fellow man so much good as to teach the truth about the benefits to the workmen from increased outputs, — for increased outputs are the one thing, or condition, that will permit raising wages permanently and reducing production costs permanently.

The benefits to the workman from raising wages speaks for itself. The benefits to the worker from reduced cost of production are not so obvious, but just as real, for when production costs are lowered the condition is made that creates greater "working opportunity." Furthermore, reduced costs of production mean greater purchasing power of the wages of the workman, and reduced costs of living.

Scientific Management eliminates human waste as does nothing else.

Let us not be wasteful in earning money, even though

we may be wasteful in spending it for those things individually most desired.

"Give back the singing man !" and give him something to sing about and to sing with, and give him plenty of hours in which to sing, and furnish him with conditions during his work hours that will make him feel like singing after his day's work is done; and during the reduced number of working hours concentrate on how to eliminate human waste, unnecessary fatigue, and the workman's presence under working conditions any longer than is necessary to achieve the proper sized day's work.

INDEX

105